TEACHER'S GUIDE

P9-DBM-321

Connected Mathematics 2™

Filling and Wrapping

Three-Dimensional Measurement

Glenda Lappan
James T. Fey
William M. Fitzgerald
Susan N. Friel
Elizabeth Difanis Phillips

PEARSON

Boston, Massachusetts · Glenview, Illinois · Shoreview, Minnesota · Upper Saddle River, New Jersey

Connected Mathematics™ was developed at Michigan State University with financial support from the Michigan State University Office of the Provost, Computing and Technology, and the College of Natural Science.

This material is based upon work supported by the National Science Foundation under Grant No. MDR 9150217 and Grant No. ESI 9986372. Opinions expressed are those of the authors and not necessarily those of the Foundation.

The Michigan State University authors and administration have agreed that all MSU royalties arising from this publication will be devoted to purposes supported by the Department of Mathematics and the MSU Mathematics Enrichment Fund.

13-digit ISBN 978-0-13-366198-9
10-digit ISBN 0-13-366198-9
1 2 3 4 5 6 7 8 9 10   11 10 09 08

Authors of Connected Mathematics

(from left to right) Glenda Lappan, Betty Phillips, Susan Friel, Bill Fitzgerald, Jim Fey

Glenda Lappan is a University Distinguished Professor in the Department of Mathematics at Michigan State University. Her research and development interests are in the connected areas of students' learning of mathematics and mathematics teachers' professional growth and change related to the development and enactment of K–12 curriculum materials.

James T. Fey is a Professor of Curriculum and Instruction and Mathematics at the University of Maryland. His consistent professional interest has been development and research focused on curriculum materials that engage middle and high school students in problem-based collaborative investigations of mathematical ideas and their applications.

William M. Fitzgerald (*Deceased*) was a Professor in the Department of Mathematics at Michigan State University. His early research was on the use of concrete materials in supporting student learning and led to the development of teaching materials for laboratory environments. Later he helped develop a teaching model to support student experimentation with mathematics.

Susan N. Friel is a Professor of Mathematics Education in the School of Education at the University of North Carolina at Chapel Hill. Her research interests focus on statistics education for middle-grade students and, more broadly, on teachers' professional development and growth in teaching mathematics K–8.

Elizabeth Difanis Phillips is a Senior Academic Specialist in the Mathematics Department of Michigan State University. She is interested in teaching and learning mathematics for both teachers and students. These interests have led to curriculum and professional development projects at the middle school and high school levels, as well as projects related to the teaching and learning of algebra across the grades.

CMP2 Development Staff

Teacher Collaborator in Residence
Yvonne Grant
Michigan State University

Production and Field Site Manager
Lisa Keller
Michigan State University

Administrative Assistant
Judith Martus Miller
Michigan State University

Technical and Editorial Support
Brin Keller, Peter Lappan, Jim Laser,
Michael Masterson, Stacey Miceli

Assessment Team
June Bailey and Debra Sobko (Apollo Middle School, Rochester, New York), George Bright (University of North Carolina, Greensboro), Gwen Ranzau Campbell (Sunrise Park Middle School, White Bear Lake, Minnesota), Holly DeRosia, Kathy Dole, and Teri Keusch (Portland Middle School, Portland, Michigan), Mary Beth Schmitt (Traverse City East Junior High School, Traverse City, Michigan), Genni Steele (Central Middle School, White Bear Lake, Minnesota), Jacqueline Stewart (Okemos, Michigan), Elizabeth Tye (Magnolia Junior High School, Magnolia, Arkansas)

Development Assistants

At Lansing Community College *Undergraduate Assistant:* James Brinegar

At Michigan State University *Graduate Assistants:* Dawn Berk, Emily Bouck, Bulent Buyukbozkirli, Kuo-Liang Chang, Christopher Danielson, Srinivasa Dharmavaram, Deb Johanning, Wesley Kretzschmar, Kelly Rivette, Sarah Sword, Tat Ming Sze, Marie Turini, Jeffrey Wanko; *Undergraduate Assistants:* Daniel Briggs, Jeffrey Chapin, Jade Corsé, Elisha Hardy, Alisha Harold, Elizabeth Keusch, Julia Letoutchaia, Karen Loeffler, Brian Oliver, Carl Oliver, Evonne Pedawi, Lauren Rebrovich

At the University of Maryland *Graduate Assistants:* Kim Harris Bethea, Kara Karch

At the University of North Carolina (Chapel Hill) *Graduate Assistants:* Mark Ellis, Trista Stearns; *Undergraduate Assistant:* Daniel Smith

Advisory Board for CMP2

Thomas Banchoff
Professor of Mathematics
Brown University
Providence, Rhode Island

Anne Bartel
Mathematics Coordinator
Minneapolis Public Schools
Minneapolis, Minnesota

Hyman Bass
Professor of Mathematics
University of Michigan
Ann Arbor, Michigan

Joan Ferrini-Mundy
Associate Dean of the College of
Natural Science; Professor
Michigan State University
East Lansing, Michigan

James Hiebert
Professor
University of Delaware
Newark, Delaware

Susan Hudson Hull
Charles A. Dana Center
University of Texas
Austin, Texas

Michele Luke
Mathematics Curriculum
Coordinator
West Junior High
Minnetonka, Minnesota

Kay McClain
Assistant Professor of
Mathematics Education
Vanderbilt University
Nashville, Tennessee

Edward Silver
Professor; Chair of Educational
Studies
University of Michigan
Ann Arbor, Michigan

Judith Sowder
Professor Emerita
San Diego State University
San Diego, California

Lisa Usher
Mathematics Resource Teacher
California Academy of
Mathematics and Science
San Pedro, California

Field Test Sites for CMP2

During the development of the revised edition of *Connected Mathematics* (CMP2), more than 100 classroom teachers have field-tested materials at 49 school sites in 12 states and the District of Columbia. This classroom testing occurred over three academic years (2001 through 2004), allowing careful study of the effectiveness of each of the 24 units that comprise the program. A special thanks to the students and teachers at these pilot schools.

Arkansas

Magnolia Public Schools
Kittena Bell*, Judith Trowell*; *Central Elementary School:* Maxine Broom, Betty Eddy, Tiffany Fallin, Bonnie Flurry, Carolyn Monk, Elizabeth Tye; *Magnolia Junior High School:* Monique Bryan, Ginger Cook, David Graham, Shelby Lamkin

Colorado

Boulder Public Schools
Nevin Platt Middle School: Judith Koenig

St. Vrain Valley School District, Longmont
Westview Middle School: Colleen Beyer, Kitty Canupp, Ellie Decker*, Peggy McCarthy, Tanya deNobrega, Cindy Payne, Ericka Pilon, Andrew Roberts

District of Columbia

Capitol Hill Day School: Ann Lawrence

Georgia

University of Georgia, Athens
Brad Findell

Madison Public Schools
Morgan County Middle School: Renee Burgdorf, Lynn Harris, Nancy Kurtz, Carolyn Stewart

Maine

Falmouth Public Schools
Falmouth Middle School: Donna Erikson, Joyce Hebert, Paula Hodgkins, Rick Hogan, David Legere, Cynthia Martin, Barbara Stiles, Shawn Towle*

Michigan

Portland Public Schools
Portland Middle School: Mark Braun, Holly DeRosia, Kathy Dole*, Angie Foote, Teri Keusch, Tammi Wardwell

Traverse City Area Public Schools
Bertha Vos Elementary: Kristin Sak; *Central Grade School:* Michelle Clark; Jody Meyers; *Eastern Elementary:* Karrie Tufts; *Interlochen Elementary:* Mary McGee-Cullen; *Long Lake Elementary:* Julie Faulkner*, Charlie Maxbauer, Katherine Sleder; *Norris Elementary:* Hope Slanaker; *Oak Park Elementary:* Jessica Steed; *Traverse Heights Elementary:* Jennifer Wolfert; *Westwoods Elementary:* Nancy Conn; *Old Mission Peninsula School:* Deb Larimer; *Traverse City East Junior High:* Ivanka Berkshire, Ruthanne Kladder, Jan Palkowski, Jane Peterson, Mary Beth Schmitt; *Traverse City West Junior High:* Dan Fouch*, Ray Fouch

Sturgis Public Schools
Sturgis Middle School: Ellen Eisele

Minnesota

Burnsville School District 191
Hidden Valley Elementary: Stephanie Cin, Jane McDevitt

Hopkins School District 270
Alice Smith Elementary: Sandra Cowing, Kathleen Gustafson, Martha Mason, Scott Stillman; *Eisenhower Elementary:* Chad Bellig, Patrick Berger, Nancy Glades, Kye Johnson, Shane Wasserman, Victoria Wilson; *Gatewood Elementary:* Sarah Ham, Julie Kloos, Janine Pung, Larry Wade; *Glen Lake Elementary:* Jacqueline Cramer, Kathy Hering, Cecelia Morris,

Robb Trenda; *Katherine Curren Elementary:* Diane Bancroft, Sue DeWit, John Wilson; *L. H. Tanglen Elementary:* Kevin Athmann, Lisa Becker, Mary LaBelle, Kathy Rezac, Roberta Severson; *Meadowbrook Elementary:* Jan Gauger, Hildy Shank, Jessica Zimmerman; *North Junior High:* Laurel Hahn, Kristin Lee, Jodi Markuson, Bruce Mestemacher, Laurel Miller, Bonnie Rinker, Jeannine Salzer, Sarah Shafer, Cam Stottler; *West Junior High:* Alicia Beebe, Kristie Earl, Nobu Fujii, Pam Georgetti, Susan Gilbert, Regina Nelson Johnson, Debra Lindstrom, Michele Luke*, Jon Sorensen

Minneapolis School District 1
Ann Sullivan K–8 School: Bronwyn Collins; Anne Bartel* (Curriculum and Instruction Office)

Wayzata School District 284
Central Middle School: Sarajane Myers, Dan Nielsen, Tanya Ravnholdt

White Bear Lake School District 624
Central Middle School: Amy Jorgenson, Michelle Reich, Brenda Sammon

New York

New York City Public Schools
IS 89: Yelena Aynbinder, Chi-Man Ng, Nina Rapaport, Joel Spengler, Phyllis Tam*, Brent Wyso; *Wagner Middle School:* Jason Appel, Intissar Fernandez, Yee Gee Get, Richard Goldstein, Irving Marcus, Sue Norton, Bernadita Owens, Jennifer Rehn*, Kevin Yuhas

---

* indicates a Field Test Site Coordinator

Ohio

Talawanda School District, Oxford
Talawanda Middle School: Teresa Abrams, Larry Brock, Heather Brosey, Julie Churchman, Monna Even, Karen Fitch, Bob George, Amanda Klee, Pat Meade, Sandy Montgomery, Barbara Sherman, Lauren Steidl

Miami University
Jeffrey Wanko*

Springfield Public Schools
Rockway School: Jim Mamer

Pennsylvania

Pittsburgh Public Schools
Kenneth Labuskes, Marianne O'Connor, Mary Lynn Raith*; *Arthur J. Rooney Middle School:* David Hairston, Stamatina Mousetis, Alfredo Zangaro; *Frick International Studies Academy:* Suzanne Berry, Janet Falkowski, Constance Finseth, Romika Hodge, Frank Machi; *Reizenstein Middle School:* Jeff Baldwin, James Brautigam, Lorena Burnett, Glen Cobbett, Michael Jordan, Margaret Lazur, Tamar McPherson, Melissa Munnell, Holly Neely, Ingrid Reed, Dennis Reft

Texas

Austin Independent School District
Bedichek Middle School: Lisa Brown, Jennifer Glasscock, Vicki Massey

El Paso Independent School District
Cordova Middle School: Armando Aguirre, Anneliesa Durkes, Sylvia Guzman, Pat Holguin*, William Holguin, Nancy Nava, Laura Orozco, Michelle Peña, Roberta Rosen, Patsy Smith, Jeremy Wolf

Plano Independent School District
Patt Henry, James Wohlgehagen*; *Frankford Middle School:* Mandy Baker, Cheryl Butsch, Amy Dudley, Betsy Eshelman, Janet Greene, Cort Haynes, Kathy Letchworth, Kay Marshall, Kelly McCants, Amy Reck, Judy Scott, Syndy Snyder, Lisa Wang; *Wilson Middle School:* Darcie Bane, Amanda Bedenko, Whitney Evans, Tonelli Hatley, Sarah (Becky) Higgs, Kelly Johnston, Rebecca McElligott, Kay Neuse, Cheri Slocum, Kelli Straight

Washington

Evergreen School District
Shahala Middle School: Nicole Abrahamsen, Terry Coon*, Carey Doyle, Sheryl Drechsler, George Gemma, Gina Helland, Amy Hilario, Darla Lidyard, Sean McCarthy, Tilly Meyer, Willow Nuewelt, Todd Parsons, Brian Pederson, Stan Posey, Shawn Scott, Craig Sjoberg, Lynette Sundstrom, Charles Switzer, Luke Youngblood

Wisconsin

Beaver Dam Unified School District
Beaver Dam Middle School: Jim Braemer, Jeanne Frick, Jessica Greatens, Barbara Link, Dennis McCormick, Karen Michels, Nancy Nichols*, Nancy Palm, Shelly Stelsel, Susan Wiggins

---

* indicates a Field Test Site Coordinator

Reviews of CMP to Guide Development of CMP2

Before writing for CMP2 began or field tests were conducted, the first edition of *Connected Mathematics* was submitted to the mathematics faculties of school districts from many parts of the country and to 80 individual reviewers for extensive comments.

School District Survey Reviews of CMP

Arizona
Madison School District #38 (Phoenix)

Arkansas
Cabot School District, Little Rock School District, Magnolia School District

California
Los Angeles Unified School District

Colorado
St. Vrain Valley School District (Longmont)

Florida
Leon County Schools (Tallahassee)

Illinois
School District #21 (Wheeling)

Indiana
Joseph L. Block Junior High (East Chicago)

Kentucky
Fayette County Public Schools (Lexington)

Maine
Selection of Schools

Massachusetts
Selection of Schools

Michigan
Sparta Area Schools

Minnesota
Hopkins School District

Texas
Austin Independent School District, The El Paso Collaborative for Academic Excellence, Plano Independent School District

Wisconsin
Platteville Middle School

Individual Reviewers of CMP

Arkansas
Deborah Cramer; Robby Frizzell *(Taylor)*; Lowell Lynde *(University of Arkansas, Monticello)*; Leigh Manzer *(Norfork)*; Lynne Roberts *(Emerson High School, Emerson)*; Tony Timms *(Cabot Public Schools)*; Judith Trowell *(Arkansas Department of Higher Education)*

California
José Alcantar *(Gilroy)*; Eugenie Belcher *(Gilroy)*; Marian Pasternack *(Lowman M. S. T. Center, North Hollywood)*; Susana Pezoa *(San Jose)*; Todd Rabusin *(Hollister)*; Margaret Siegfried *(Ocala Middle School, San Jose)*; Polly Underwood *(Ocala Middle School, San Jose)*

Colorado
Janeane Golliher *(St. Vrain Valley School District, Longmont)*; Judith Koenig *(Nevin Platt Middle School, Boulder)*

Florida
Paige Loggins *(Swift Creek Middle School, Tallahassee)*

Illinois
Jan Robinson *(School District #21, Wheeling)*

Indiana
Frances Jackson *(Joseph L. Block Junior High, East Chicago)*

Kentucky
Natalee Feese *(Fayette County Public Schools, Lexington)*

Maine
Betsy Berry *(Maine Math & Science Alliance, Augusta)*

Maryland
Joseph Gagnon *(University of Maryland, College Park)*; Paula Maccini *(University of Maryland, College Park)*

Massachusetts
George Cobb *(Mt. Holyoke College, South Hadley)*; Cliff Kanold *(University of Massachusetts, Amherst)*

Michigan
Mary Bouck *(Farwell Area Schools)*; Carol Dorer *(Slauson Middle School, Ann Arbor)*; Carrie Heaney *(Forsythe Middle School, Ann Arbor)*; Ellen Hopkins *(Clague Middle School, Ann Arbor)*; Teri Keusch *(Portland Middle School, Portland)*; Valerie Mills *(Oakland Schools, Waterford)*; Mary Beth Schmitt *(Traverse City East Junior High, Traverse City)*; Jack Smith *(Michigan State University, East Lansing)*; Rebecca Spencer *(Sparta Middle School, Sparta)*; Ann Marie Nicoll Turner *(Tappan Middle School, Ann Arbor)*; Scott Turner *(Scarlett Middle School, Ann Arbor)*

Minnesota
Margarita Alvarez *(Olson Middle School, Minneapolis)*; Jane Amundson *(Nicollet Junior High, Burnsville)*; Anne Bartel *(Minneapolis Public Schools)*; Gwen Ranzau Campbell *(Sunrise Park Middle School, White Bear Lake)*; Stephanie Cin *(Hidden Valley Elementary, Burnsville)*; Joan Garfield *(University of Minnesota, Minneapolis)*; Gretchen Hall *(Richfield Middle School, Richfield)*; Jennifer Larson *(Olson Middle School, Minneapolis)*; Michele Luke *(West Junior High, Minnetonka)*; Jeni Meyer *(Richfield Junior High, Richfield)*; Judy Pfingsten *(Inver Grove Heights Middle School, Inver Grove Heights)*; Sarah Shafer *(North Junior High, Minnetonka)*; Genni Steele *(Central Middle School, White Bear Lake)*; Victoria Wilson *(Eisenhower Elementary, Hopkins)*; Paul Zorn *(St. Olaf College, Northfield)*

New York
Debra Altenau-Bartolino *(Greenwich Village Middle School, New York)*; Doug Clements *(University of Buffalo)*; Francis Curcio *(New York University, New York)*; Christine Dorosh *(Clinton School for Writers, Brooklyn)*; Jennifer Rehn *(East Side Middle School, New York)*; Phyllis Tam *(IS 89 Lab School, New York)*;

Marie Turini *(Louis Armstrong Middle School, New York)*; Lucy West *(Community School District 2, New York)*; Monica Witt *(Simon Baruch Intermediate School 104, New York)*

Pennsylvania
Robert Aglietti *(Pittsburgh)*; Sharon Mihalich *(Freeport)*; Jennifer Plumb *(South Hills Middle School, Pittsburgh)*; Mary Lynn Raith *(Pittsburgh Public Schools)*

Texas
Michelle Bittick *(Austin Independent School District)*; Margaret Cregg *(Plano Independent School District)*; Sheila Cunningham *(Klein Independent School District)*; Judy Hill *(Austin Independent School District)*; Patricia Holguin *(El Paso Independent School District)*; Bonnie McNemar *(Arlington)*; Kay Neuse *(Plano Independent School District)*; Joyce Polanco *(Austin Independent School District)*; Marge Ramirez *(University of Texas at El Paso)*; Pat Rossman *(Baker Campus, Austin)*; Cindy Schimek *(Houston)*; Cynthia Schneider *(Charles A. Dana Center, University of Texas at Austin)*; Uri Treisman *(Charles A. Dana Center, University of Texas at Austin)*; Jacqueline Weilmuenster *(Grapevine-Colleyville Independent School District)*; LuAnn Weynand *(San Antonio)*; Carmen Whitman *(Austin Independent School District)*; James Wohlgehagen *(Plano Independent School District)*

Washington
Ramesh Gangolli *(University of Washington, Seattle)*

Wisconsin
Susan Lamon *(Marquette University, Hales Corner)*; Steve Reinhart *(retired, Chippewa Falls Middle School, Eau Claire)*

Filling and Wrapping
Three-Dimensional Measurement

The Student Edition pages for the Unit Opener follow page 12.

Filling and Wrapping
Three-Dimensional Measurement

Goals of the Unit

In *Filling and Wrapping*, we will explore surface area and volume of objects, especially rectangular prisms, cylinders, cones, and spheres. The unit should help students to

- Understand volume as a measure of *filling* an object and surface area as a measure of *wrapping* an object

- Design and use nets to visualize and calculate surface areas of prisms and cylinders

- Explore patterns among the volumes of cylinders, cones, and spheres

- Develop strategies for finding the volumes of square pyramids, prisms, cylinders, cones, and spheres directly and by comparison with known volumes

- Understand that three-dimensional figures may have the same volume but quite different surface areas

- Understand how changes in one or more dimensions of a rectangular prism or cylinder affects the prism's volume and surface area

- Extend students' understanding of similarity and scale factors to three-dimensional figures

- Use surface area and volume to solve a variety of real-world problems

Developing Students' Mathematical Habits

Throughout their work in this and other geometry units, students learn to ask important questions about volume and surface area.

- *What quantities are involved in the problem?*

- *Which measures of an object are involved—volume or surface area?*

- *Is an exact answer required?*

- *What method should I use to determine these measures?*

- *What strategies or formulas might help?*

Mathematics of the Unit

Pearson Prentice Hall
Professional
Development

Overview

In *Filling and Wrapping*, students explore the surface areas and volumes of rectangular prisms and cylinders in depth. They look informally at how changing the scale of a box affects its surface area and volume. They also informally investigate other solids—including cones, spheres, and square pyramids—to develop volume relationships.

Summary of Investigations

Investigation 1

Building Boxes

Students are introduced to the ideas of volume and surface area through the concepts of wrapping and filling, building on their knowledge of area and perimeter of two-dimensional figures from the *Covering and Surrounding* unit. Rectangular prisms are described by their dimensions: length, width, and height.

Investigation 2

Designing Rectangular Boxes

Students continue their exploration of surface area and investigate its relationship to volume. The terms *surface area* and *volume* are introduced as vocabulary. By thinking about filling boxes in layers, students develop the formula for volume of a rectangular prism. The volume of a box is the number of blocks in the bottom layer multiplied by the number of layers—the area of the base times the height of the prism. (This strategy holds for all prisms.)

Investigation 3

Prisms and Cylinders

Students compare the volumes and surface areas of a variety of prisms with regular bases and a common height. Students build prisms by folding several sheets of congruent rectangular paper into the shapes of triangular, rectangular, and

hexagonal prisms. They find the volume of any rectangular prism by determining how many unit cubes would fill the prism. They observe that the volume of a prism increases as the number of lateral sides increases. The volume of a cylinder is the area of the base (the number of unit cubes in the bottom layer) of the cylinder multiplied by its height (the number of layers). Surface area is informally looked at as the sum of the area of the bases (circles) and lateral side (rectangle).

Prisms and cylinders come together as students design a rectangular box with the *same* volume as a given cylinder. They find the surface area of the box is greater than the surface area of the cylinder.

Investigation 4

Cones, Spheres, and Pyramids

Students compare the volumes of cones, cylinders, and spheres in an application. Students determine how many times the volume of the cone or sphere will fill the cylinder and then look for relationships among the three volumes. (Finding the surface areas of cones and spheres is not considered in this unit.) Students also compare the volume of a square pyramid to a cube.

Investigation 5

Scaling Boxes

Students study the effects of changing the dimensions or the volume of a rectangular prism in the context of designing compost containers. They explore two central ideas: how to double the volume of a rectangular prism and examine how other measures change as a result, and the effects of applying scale factors to the dimensions of rectangular prisms. What effect does doubling (tripling, quadrupling, etc.) each dimension of a rectangular container have on its volume and surface area? Students apply their knowledge of similarity and scale factors to explore the relationships between a model of a cruise ship and the actual cruise ship. This last problem connects many of the ideas discussed in this unit.

Mathematics Background

Rectangular Prisms

Students begin the unit by exploring the surface area of a rectangular box. The strategy for finding the surface area of a box is to determine the total area needed to wrap the container. Students create nets that can be folded into boxes. The area of the net becomes the surface area of the box.

This provides a visual representation of surface area as a two-dimensional measure of a three-dimensional object.

In the student edition, a rectangular prism is defined as a three-dimensional shape with six rectangular faces. Technically, this defines a **right rectangular prism**. An **oblique rectangular prism** also has opposite sides that are rectangles, but at least two opposite sides must be nonrectangular parallelograms.

Oblique rectangular prism

In this unit we only discuss right rectangular prisms. There is one ACE question on oblique rectangular prisms. The following figures are right rectangular prisms drawn on isometric dot paper.

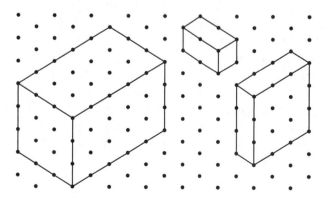

Isometric drawings are another useful 2-dimensional representation of 3-dimensional objects. You may wish to have isometric dot paper available throughout the unit for students to use in making sketches of the 3-dimensional prism they create.

The strategy for finding the volume of a rectangular box is to count the number of layers of unit cubes it takes to fill the container. The number of unit cubes in a layer is equal to the area of the base—one unit cube sits on each square unit in the base. The volume (the total number of unit cubes) of a rectangular prism is the area of its base (the number of unit cubes in the first layer) multiplied by its height (the total number of layers).

one layer   **five layers fill the box**

The same layering strategy is used to generalize the method for finding the volume of any prism. The volume of any prism is the area of its base multiplied by its height.

Rectangular Prism   **Triangular Prism**   **Hexagonal Prism**

Students also informally compare the volume of two rectangular boxes by filling one box with rice or sand and then pouring the sand into the other rectangular box.

Cylinders

The surface area and volume of a cylinder are developed in a similar way. Like a prism, a cylinder has two identical faces (circles). Also like a prism, a cylinder has a lateral surface that flattens to a rectangle. Students will notice all of these similarities. If they need language for the rectangle that is part of the net of both cylinders and prisms, feel free to introduce the term *lateral surface*. The term is not included in the student materials. Students cut and fold a net to form a cylinder. In the process, they find that the surface area of the cylinder is the area of the rectangle that forms the lateral surface plus the areas of the two circular ends.

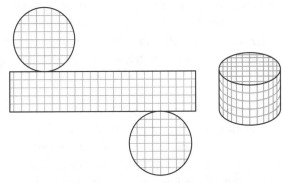

Cylinders can be thought of as circular prisms. In this case, it is easy to extend the techniques for measuring prisms to techniques for measuring cylinders. The volume of a cylinder is developed as the number of unit cubes in one layer (the area of the circular base) multiplied by the number of layers (the height) needed to fill the cylinder. Because the edge of the circular base intersects the unit cubes, students will have to estimate the number of cubes in the bottom layer.

From the *Covering and Surrounding* unit, students know the formula for the area of a circle. They can apply this formula to find the area of the base of a cylinder. The area of the base is multiplied by the height to find the volume.

The volume of a cylinder $= \pi r^2 h$. Students investigate rectangular prisms with polygonal bases. If the prisms have the same heights, then as the number of sides of the polygonal base increases, the shape gets closer to a cylinder.

Estimate the number of unit cubes in one layer.

And multiply by the number of layers.

Cones, Spheres, and Rectangular Pyramids

Students conduct an experiment to demonstrate the relationships among the volumes of a cylinder, a cone, and a sphere. If all three have the same radius and the same height (the height being equal to two radii), then it takes three cones full of sand to fill the cylinder, and one and a half spheres full of sand to fill the cylinder.

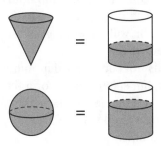

These relationships may also be expressed as follows:

volume of the cone $= \frac{1}{3}$ of the volume of the cylinder or $\frac{1}{3}\pi r^2 h$

volume of the sphere $= \frac{2}{3}$ of the volume of the cylinder or $\frac{2}{3}\pi r^2(2r)$ or $\frac{4}{3}\pi r^3$

For cones and spheres, only the volume is studied. Surface area in these two cases is not considered here because the reasoning needed would take us too far afield. Formulas for these are sometimes considered within the context of high school geometry or calculus courses.

The volume of a square pyramid is found in a similar way by comparing it to a square prism. This is easily generalized to finding the volume of a rectangular pyramid. If the base of the pyramid is a polygon, then as the number of sides of the polygon increases, the shape of the pyramid gets closer to a cone.

Relationship Between Surface Area and Fixed Volume

Students also investigate the effects of a change in dimension, surface area, or volume on the other attributes of a three-dimensional object. For example, if 24 unit cubes are arranged in a rectangular shape and packaged in a rectangular box, which arrangement of the cubes will require the least (the most) packaging material? By physically arranging the blocks and determining the surface area of each arrangement, students discover that a column of 24 cubes requires the most packaging, and the arrangement that is the most like a cube (2 by 3 by 4) requires the least amount of packaging. This is similar to ideas students have studied about plane figures: For a fixed area, the rectangle that is most like a square has the least perimeter of any rectangle with the same area. A similar relationship holds for a fixed surface area. The rectangular prism that is the most like a cube will have the greatest volume for a fixed surface area.

In fact, it is not cube-ness that minimizes surface area, but sphere-ness. For a fixed volume, a sphere has the smallest surface area and, conversely for a fixed surface area, a sphere has the largest volume.

Effects of Changing Attributes— Similar Prisms

Through the context of designing an indoor compost box, students explore the effects that changing a box's dimension have on the volume and surface area of the box. Given the dimensions of a compost box known to decompose a half pound of garbage per day, students investigate what size box would decompose one pound of garbage per day. They find that they need to double only one dimension of a rectangular box to double its volume.

Students also look at the effects of doubling all three dimensions of a box. Making scale models of the original box and the new box helps students visualize the effect of the scale factor. Doubling each dimension of a rectangular prism increases the surface area by $2 \times 2 = 4$ times (a scale factor of 2^2) and volume by $2 \times 2 \times 2 = 8$ times (a scale factor of 2^3). The surfaces of the two prisms are similar figures with a scale factor of 2 from the small prism to the large prism. This exploration connects back to ideas in the similarity unit, *Stretching and Shrinking*.

When we describe a cylinder, we generally give only two dimensions: the height and the radius. The radius is constant in every direction, so we need not give a "length radius" and a "width radius." Yet, when we change the radius, we change both the length and the width of the base. That is, we change two dimensions, not just one. In the ACE for Investigation 5, students investigate similar cylinders. At that point, students may need to discuss whether a cylinder is 2- or 3-dimensional in this sense.

Measurement

All measurements are approximations. In the work in this unit, this idea will become more apparent than usual. Students' calculations of surface area and volume will often involve an approximation of the number π, and they will often use a calculated amount as a value in a subsequent calculation. Be aware that although students' answers will often differ. The answers may reflect correct reasoning and correct mathematics.

Content Connections to Other Units

Big Idea	Prior Work	Future Work
Interpreting volume as the number of unit cubes that *fill* a 3-dimensional figure	Interpreting area as the number of squares that cover a 2-dimensional figure (*Covering and Surrounding*); making minimal and maximal buildings (*Ruins of Montarek © 2004*); studying relationships between 3-D models and 2-D representations of the models (*Ruins of Montarek © 2004*)	
Interpreting surface area as the number of square units that cover or *wrap* the exterior of a 3-dimensional figure	Interpreting perimeter as the number of linear units that surround a 2-dimensional figure (*Covering and Surrounding*); interpreting area as the number of squares that cover a 2-dimensional figure (*Covering and Surrounding*)	
Developing strategies for finding and comparing volumes and surface areas of different 3-dimensional figures	Comparing areas and perimeters of different 2-dimensional figures (*Covering and Surrounding*)	
Studying the relationships among the dimensions, surface area, and volume of prisms and cylinders	Studying the relationship between perimeter and area in rectangles (*Covering and Surrounding*)	Algebraically analyzing such relationships in geometric figures (*Frogs, Fleas, and Painted Cubes*)
Developing strategies and algorithms for finding the surface area and volume of prisms and cones, and the volume of cones and spheres	Developing strategies and algorithms for finding the perimeter and area of rectangles, triangles, parallelograms, and circles (*Covering and Surrounding*)	Using variables to represent a variety of relationships algebraically (*Moving Straight Ahead; Frogs, Fleas, and Painted Cubes; Growing, Growing, Growing; Say It With Symbols*)
Studying the effects of applying scale factor to the dimensions of a prism to its volume and surface area	Enlarging, shrinking, and distorting 2-D figures (*Stretching and Shrinking*); scaling quantities up and down using ratios and proportions (*Comparing and Scaling*)	

Pacing Suggestions and Materials

Investigations and Assessments	Pacing 45–50 min. classes	Materials for Students	Materials for Teachers
1 Building Boxes	$4\frac{1}{2}$ days	Assortment of boxes, scissors, inch and cm cubes, inch and cm grid paper, Labsheet 1.3, rulers, tape	Transparencies 1.1A and 1.1B (optional), and 1.3A and 1.3B, 2 or 3 rectangular boxes, inch cubes (optional)
Mathematical Reflections	$\frac{1}{2}$ day		
2 Designing Rectangular Boxes	$3\frac{1}{2}$ days	Inch cubes, unit cubes (optional), boxes	Transparencies 2.1, 2.3A–C, nets and boxes from Investigation 1, rectangular or cubic boxes, Boxes W, X, Y, and Z (optional)
Mathematical Reflections	$\frac{1}{2}$ day		
Assessment: Check Up 1	$\frac{1}{2}$ day		
3 Prisms and Cylinders	$4\frac{1}{2}$ days	Scissors, blank paper, tape, inch cubes, inch grid paper, cylinders, Labsheet 3.2, 3.3A and 3.3B, cm grid paper, colored pencils or markers, transparent tape	Transparencies 3.1, 3.2A, 3.2B, 3.3A, and 3.3B, sample prisms and unit cubes, sheets of paper, macaroni or rice, cm cubes, cylindrical and/or rectangular juice containers (optional)
Mathematical Reflections	$\frac{1}{2}$ day		
Assessment: Quiz	1 day		
4 Cones, Spheres, and Pyramids	4 days	Modeling dough; transparent plastic; scissors; tape; Labsheets 4.1, 4.2A–E; stiff paper; sand or rice; cylinders made in 4.1	Transparencies 4.1A, 4.1B, 4.2, 4.3, cylinders, models of a prism and pyramid with the same base and height, ice cream cone and cylindrical cup (optional)
Mathematical Reflections	$\frac{1}{2}$ day		
Assessment: Check Up 2	$\frac{1}{2}$ day		
5 Scaling Boxes	$3\frac{1}{2}$ days	Grid paper, scissors, tape, Labsheet 5.2, boxes from 5.1 (optional)	Article clip, Transparency 5.2, 1-2-3 and 2-4-6 boxes
Mathematical Reflections	$\frac{1}{2}$ day		
Looking Back and Looking Ahead	1 day		
Assessment: Unit Project	Optional		
Assessment: Self Assessment	Take Home		
Assessment: Unit Test	1 day		

Total Time	$26\frac{1}{2}$ days	**Materials for Use in All Investigations**	
For detailed pacing for Problems within each Investigation, see the Suggested Pacing at the beginning of each Investigation. For pacing with block scheduling, see next page.		Calculators, blank transparencies and transparency markers (optional), student notebooks	Blank transparencies and transparency markers (optional)

Pacing for Block Scheduling (90-minute class periods)

Investigation	Suggested Pacing	Investigation	Suggested Pacing	Investigation	Suggested Pacing
Investigation 1	**$2\frac{1}{2}$ days**	**Investigation 3**	**3 days**	**Investigation 5**	**2 days**
Problem 1.1	$\frac{1}{2}$ day	Problem 3.1	$\frac{1}{2}$ day	Problem 5.1	$\frac{1}{2}$ day
Problem 1.2	$\frac{1}{2}$ day	Problem 3.2	$\frac{1}{2}$ day	Problem 5.2	$\frac{1}{2}$ day
Problem 1.3	$\frac{1}{2}$ day	Problem 3.3	$\frac{1}{2}$ day	Problem 5.3	$\frac{1}{2}$ day
Problem 1.4	$\frac{1}{2}$ day	Problem 3.4	1 day	Math Reflections	$\frac{1}{2}$ day
Math Reflections	$\frac{1}{2}$ day	Math Reflections	$\frac{1}{2}$ day		
Investigation 2	**2 days**	**Investigation 4**	**2 days**		
Problem 2.1	$\frac{1}{2}$ day	Problem 4.1	$\frac{1}{2}$ day		
Problem 2.2	$\frac{1}{2}$ day	Problem 4.2	$\frac{1}{2}$ day		
Problem 2.3	$\frac{1}{2}$ day	Problem 4.3	$\frac{1}{2}$ day		
Math Reflections	$\frac{1}{2}$ day	Math Reflections	$\frac{1}{2}$ day		

Vocabulary

Essential Terms Developed in This Unit		Useful Terms Referenced in This Unit		Terms Developed in Previous Units
base	prism	area	radius	right prism
cone	pyramid	circumference	width	oblique prism
cylinder	rectangular prism	congruent		
dimensions	sphere	height		
edge	surface area	length		
face	unit cube	perimeter		
net	volume	pi (π)		

For: Teacher Resources
Web Code: ank-5500

Components

Use the chart below to quickly see which components are available for each Investigation.

Investigation	Labsheets	Additional Practice	Transparencies		Formal Assessment		Assessment Options	
			Problem	**Summary**	**Check Up**	**Partner Quiz**	**Multiple-Choice**	**Question Bank**
1	1.3	✔	1.1A–B, 1.3A–B				✔	✔
2		✔	2.1, 2.3A–C		✔		✔	✔
3	3.2, 3.3A, 3.3B	✔	3.1, 3.2A–B, 3.3A–B			✔	✔	✔
4	4.1, 4.2A–E	✔	4.1A–B, 4.2, 4.3		✔		✔	✔
5	5.2	✔	5.2				✔	✔
For the Unit		*ExamView* CD-ROM, Web site	LBLA		Unit Test, Notebook Check, Self Assessment		Multiple-Choice, Question Bank, *ExamView* CD-ROM	

Also Available for Use With This Unit

- Parent Guide: take-home letter for the unit
- Implementing CMP
- Spanish Assessment Resources
- Additional online and technology resources

Technology

The Use of Calculators

Connected Mathematics was developed with the belief that calculators should be available and that students should learn when their use is appropriate. For this reason, we do not designate specific problems as "calculator problems." The calculations in *Filling and Wrapping* involve only simple arithmetic, so nonscientific calculators are adequate.

Several formulas are developed in this unit. These formulas, together with the use of calculators, provide an opportunity to discuss order of operations.

Student Activity CD-ROM

Includes interactive activities to enhance the learning in the Problems within Investigations.

PHSchool.com

For Students Multiple-choice practice with instant feedback, updated data sources, Tinkerplots software for data analysis.

For Teachers Professional development, curriculum support, downloadable forms, and more.

See also www.math.msu.edu/cmp for more resources for both teachers and students.

ExamView® CD-ROM

Create multiple versions of practice sheets and tests for course objectives and standardized tests. Includes dynamic questions, online testing, student reports, and all test and practice items in Spanish. Also includes all items in the *Assessment Resources* and *Additional Practice*.

TeacherExpress™ CD-ROM

Includes a lesson planning tool, the Teacher's Guide pages, and all the teaching resources.

LessonLab Online Courses

LessonLab offers comprehensive, facilitated professional development designed to help teachers implement CMP2 and improve student achievement. To learn more, please visit PHSchool.com/cmp2.

Assessment Summary

Ongoing Informal Assessment

Embedded in the Student Unit

Problems Use students' work from the Problems to check student understanding.

ACE exercises Use ACE exercises for homework assignments to assess student understanding.

Mathematical Reflections Have students summarize their learning at the end of each Investigation.

Looking Back and Looking Ahead At the end of the unit, use the first two sections to allow students to show what they know about the unit.

Additional Resources

Teacher's Edition Use the Check for Understanding feature of some Summaries and the probing questions that appear in the *Launch, Explore,* or *Summarize* sections of all Investigations to check student understanding.

Self Assessment

Notebook Check Students use this tool to organize and check their notebooks before giving them to their teacher. Located in *Assessment Resources.*

Self Assessment At the end of the unit, students reflect on and provide examples of what they learned. Located in *Assessment Resources.*

Formal Assessment

Choose the assessment materials that are appropriate for your students.

Assessment	For Use After	Focus	Student Work
Check Up 1	Invest. 2	Skills	Individual
Partner Quiz	Invest. 3	Rich problems	Pair
Check Up 2	Invest. 4	Skills	Individual
Unit Test	The Unit	Skills, rich problems	Individual
Unit Project	The Unit	Rich problems	Group

Additional Resources

Multiple-Choice Items Use these items for homework, review, a quiz, or add them to the Unit Test.

Question Bank Choose from these questions for homework, review, or replacements for Quiz, Check Up, or Unit Test questions.

Additional Practice Choose practice exercises for each investigation for homework, review, or formal assessments.

ExamView **CD-ROM** Create practice sheets, review quizzes, and tests with this dynamic software. Give online tests and receive student progress reports. (All test items are also available in Spanish.)

Spanish Assessment Resources

Includes Partner Quizzes, Check Ups, Unit Test, Multiple-Choice Items, Question Bank, Notebook Check, and Self Assessment. Plus, the *ExamView* CD-ROM has all test items in Spanish.

Correlation to Standardized Tests

Investigation	NAEP	Terra Nova CAT6	Terra Nova CTBS	ITBS	SAT10	Local Test
1 Building Boxes	M1h	✔	✔		✔	
2 Designing Rectangular Boxes	M1j	✔	✔			
3 Prisms and Cylinders	G1c, G1e, G1f	✔	✔	✔	✔	
4 Cones, Spheres, and Pyramids	M1j		✔			
5 Scaling Boxes	M2b, M2c					

NAEP National Assessment of Educational Progress

CAT6/Terra Nova California Achievement Test, 6th Ed.
CTBS/Terra Nova Comprehensive Test of Basic Skills

ITBS Iowa Test of Basic Skills, Form M
SAT10 Stanford Achievement Test, 10th Ed.

Introducing Your Students to *Filling and Wrapping*

One way to introduce your students to this unit is to ask them to think about measurement. What aspects of a classroom could we measure? Examples might include the temperature, the number of students that can fit inside, the height of the ceiling, etc. When students mention *size*, press them to be specific about how to measure size. What do they mean when they say one classroom is larger than another? Tell students that in this unit, we will focus on two measures: volume and surface area. Listen to what students already know about these measurements.

Using the Unit Opener

Discuss the questions posed on the opening page of the Student Edition, which are designed to start students thinking about the kinds of questions and mathematics in the unit. Don't look for "correct" answers at this time. Do, however, present an opportunity for the class to discuss the questions and to start to think about what is needed to answer them. You may want to revisit these questions as students learn the mathematical ideas and techniques necessary to find the answers.

Problems in contexts are used to help students reason about the mathematics of the unit. The problems are deliberately sequenced to develop understanding of concepts and skills.

Using the Unit Project

The optional unit project gives students an opportunity to apply what they have learned about volume and surface area in a real-world application problem. In the project, the fictitious Worldwide Sporting Company is sponsoring a contest for the design of three packages to hold standard table-tennis balls. To enter the Package Design Contest, students are to submit three package designs and a written explanation of the designs to the company.

See the Guide to the Unit Project section on page 115 for more information about assigning and assessing the project. There you will find a suggested scoring rubric and samples of student projects. Each sample is followed by a teacher's comments about assessing the project.

Using the Mathematical Highlights

The Mathematical Highlights page in the Student Edition provides information to students, parents, and other family members. It gives students a preview of the mathematics and some of the overarching questions that they should ask themselves while studying *Filling and Wrapping*.

As they work through the unit, students can refer back to the Mathematical Highlights page to review what they have learned and to preview what is still to come. This page also tells students' families what mathematical ideas and activities will be covered as the class works through *Filling and Wrapping*.

Connected Mathematics 2™

Filling and Wrapping

Three-Dimensional Measurement

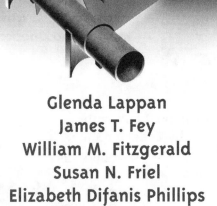

Glenda Lappan
James T. Fey
William M. Fitzgerald
Susan N. Friel
Elizabeth Difanis Phillips

PEARSON

Boston, Massachusetts · Glenview, Illinois · Shoreview, Minnesota · Upper Saddle River, New Jersey

Notes _____

_____

_____

_____

Filling and Wrapping

Three-Dimensional Measurement

Baseballs, basketballs, and soccer balls are spheres, but they often come in boxes shaped liked cubes. Why do you think balls are packaged in this way?

A popcorn vendor needs to order popcorn boxes. A rectangular box has a height of 20 centimeters and a square base with 12-centimeter sides. A cylindrical box has a height of 20 centimeters and a diameter of 12 centimeters. Which box will hold the most popcorn?

A rectangular compost box with dimensions 1 foot by 2 feet by 3 feet can decompose 0.5 pounds of garbage a day. Describe the dimensions of a box that will decompose 1 pound of garbage a day.

2   Filling and Wrapping

Notes _____

_____

_____

_____

The way a product is packaged is important. Stores are filled with interesting three-dimensional shapes such as boxes, cans, bags, and bottles. A unique shape can attract shoppers to take a closer look at the product. When a company plans the packaging for a product, it must consider several questions, including how much of the product should be sold in each package; what and how much material is needed to make the package; and what package design is best for the product.

Thinking about how products are packaged can make you a smarter consumer. You can usually save money by comparing the cost of products in different-sized packages.

In this unit, you will look at two different measures involved in three-dimensional shapes. You will explore how much material it takes to *fill* a shape and how much material is needed to *wrap* a shape. As you work through the investigation, you will consider questions like those on the opposite page.

Notes _____

_____

_____

_____

Mathematical Highlights

Making Sense of Symbols

In *Filling and Wrapping*, you will explore surface area and volume of objects, especially rectangular prisms, cylinders, cones, and spheres.

You will learn how to

- Understand volume as a measure of *filling* an object and surface area as a measure of *wrapping* an object
- Develop strategies for finding the volume and surface area of objects including rectangular prisms and cylinders
- Develop strategies for finding the volume of square pyramids, cones, and spheres
- Explore patterns among the volumes of cylinders, cones, and spheres
- Design and use nets for rectangular prisms and cylinders to calculate surface areas of prisms and cylinders
- Understand that three-dimensional figures may have the same volume but different surface areas
- Investigate the effects of varying dimensions of rectangular prisms and cylinders on volume and surface area
- Recognize and solve problems involving volume and surface area

As you work on problems in this unit, ask yourself questions about volume and surface area.

What quantities are involved in the problem? Which measures of an object are involved—volume or surface area?

Is an exact answer required?

What method should I use to determine these measures?

What strategies or formulas might help?

Notes _____

_____

_____

_____

Building Boxes

Mathematical and Problem-Solving Goals

- Visualize a net as a representation of the surface area of a rectangular prism
- Connect the area of the net to the surface area of a rectangular prism
- Understand that the volume of a rectangular prism is the total number of unit cubes needed to fill it
- Understand the relationship between the dimensions of a rectangular prism and its surface area
- Develop a strategy for finding the surface area of a rectangular prism

Summary of Problems

Students are introduced to the ideas (but not yet the *vocabulary*) of volume and surface area through the concepts of filling and of wrapping. This builds on their knowledge of area and perimeter of two-dimensional figures from the grade 6 *Covering and Surrounding* unit. Rectangular prisms are described by their dimensions: length, width, and height.

Problem 1.1 Making Cubic Boxes

Students design nets for cubic boxes, fold them into boxes, and consider their areas.

Problem 1.2 Making Rectangular Boxes

Students design nets for a given non-cubic box and consider their area as well as the number of unit cubes that would fill the box.

Problem 1.3 Testing Nets

Students are given nets and asked to analyze the boxes the nets make.

Problem 1.4 Flattening a Box

Students are given a real box, for which they design a net. They then cut their boxes to unfold to match the net they drew.

	Suggested Pacing	Materials for Students	Materials for Teachers	ACE Assignments
All	5 days	Assortment of interesting boxes or containers (optional)		
1.1	1 day	Scissors; inch cubes; inch grid paper	Transparencies 1.1A and 1.1B (optional)	1–4, 15–18, 32
1.2	1 day	cm grid paper; scissors	2 or 3 rectangular boxes cm cubes (optional)	5, 6, 7, 19–24
1.3	1 day	Labsheet 1.3 (1 per student, plus extra one for group); scissors; cm cubes	Transparency 1.3A and 1.3B	8–9, 25–27, 31
1.4	$1\frac{1}{2}$ days	Small boxes (1 per pair); scissors; cm grid paper; rulers; transparent tape		10–14, 28–30, 33
MR	$\frac{1}{2}$ day			

Making Cubic Boxes

Goals

- Visualize a net as a representation of the surface area of a cube

- Connect the area of the net to the surface area of a cube

In this problem, students design nets on grid paper, cut them out, and fold them to form unit cubes. The area of each net is the surface area of the related cube. This problem helps students see the connection between the area of a flat figure and the surface area of a solid figure.

Students may use any size cube for this problem. However, larger cubes are easier to work with. Teachers recommend one-inch cubes and one-inch grid paper.

Launch 1.1

Discuss the work of packaging engineers, who design packages in which to store and ship objects. Packages are often designed under a set of constraints determined by the company and their customers. For example, keeping material use to a minimum is a frequently imposed constraint. Hold up some interesting boxes or containers and ask them to discuss what measurements might be useful for a packaging engineer.

Suggested Questions To help students begin thinking about packaging items, discuss the idea that some boxes are cubes. Have students describe a cube.

- *What does a cube look like?* (Examples: It is 3-dimensional; its sides look like squares, etc.)

- *What features of a cube could we count?* (its corners, its edges, its sides)

- *We call the corners* vertices. *How many vertices does a cube have?* (8)

- *How many edges does a cube have?* (12, although it may take some discussion to agree on this.)

- *We call the sides* faces. *How many faces does a cube have?* (6)

Introduce the term *unit cube*. This is a cube that is used to represent one unit of volume, or one cubic unit. A particular unit cube might be chosen as the basis unit for measuring volume, similar to the decision to measure length in inches or centimeters, or area in square inches or square centimeters. The chosen unit becomes the unit of measurement for a particular situation.

Make a copy of the net shown in the student edition, or cut it from Transparency 1.1A and display it on the overhead projector. Use it to review the special features that describe plane figures, such as dimensions, area, and perimeter. Perimeter is the distance around the net; area is the number of unit squares in the net. Corresponding measures will be developed for three-dimensional figures.

Be sure students understand that the cube cannot have 2 overlapping squares from the net. Have students work on the problem in groups of two or three to find other nets that will cover a unit cube. Each student should make at least one new net. They can cut them out to use in the summary.

Students can work in groups of 2–3 to share the work of finding all of the nets.

Explore 1.1

Suggested Questions As you circulate, ask students questions about the nets they are creating.

- *How do you know your nets will work?*

- *How could you show someone else that they will work?*

- *What things are the same in all of the nets?* (Example: They all have the same area. They all have 6 unit squares.)

- *What things are different?* (different arrangements of 6 square units of area)

- *How is the area of the net related to the number of squares that would be needed to cover the cube?*

Give some groups transparent grid paper to record their nets. These can be used in the summary.

Going Further Ask students to make at least three nets for a cube without a top.

Summarize 1.1

Ask students to display the various nets on the board or overhead projector. Discuss the nets that the class generated. Repeat the questions asked in the preceding Explore section.

Students may argue that some of the nets are the same (the concept of rotational symmetry is explored in the grade 6 unit *Shapes and Designs*). Two nets are identical (congruent) if one can be flipped and turned so that it fits exactly on the other figure. For example, see the following nets. They are all congruent to one another.

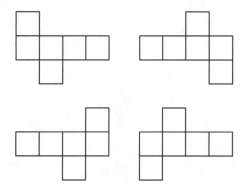

Ask the following question to get students thinking about ideas that will later lead to the concept of surface area:

● *What is the total area needed to cover a unit cube?*

You may want to use ACE Exercise 32 as an in-class wrap-up problem.

1.1 Making Cubic Boxes

Mathematical Goals

- Visualize a net as a representation of the surface area of a cube
- Connect the area of the net to the surface area of a cube

Launch

Discuss the work of packaging engineers. To help students begin thinking about packaging items, discuss with them the introduction to the investigation in the student edition. Discuss the idea that some boxes are cubes. Have students describe a cube.

- *What does a cube look like?*
- *What features of a cube could we count? We call the corners* vertices.
- *How many vertices does a cube have? How many edges does a cube have? We call the sides* faces. *How many faces does a cube have?*

Introduce the term *unit cube*. Review the special features that describe plane figures, such as dimensions, area, and perimeter. Corresponding measures will be developed for three-dimensional figures.

Be sure students understand that the cube cannot have two overlapping squares from the net.

Each student should make at least one new net. Students can work in groups of 2–3 to share the work of finding all of the nets.

Materials
- Inch grid paper
- Inch cubes
- Transparencies 1.1A and 1.1B (optional)

Vocabulary
- Unit cube
- Net
- Edge
- Face

Explore

As you circulate, ask students questions about the nets they are creating.

- *How do you know your nets will work? How could you show someone else that they will work?*
- *What things are the same in all of the nets? What things are different? How is the area of the net related to the number of squares that would be needed to cover the cube?*

Give some groups transparent grid paper to record their nets. These can be used in the summary.

Materials
- Scissors

Summarize

Ask students to display the various nets on the board or overhead projector. Discuss the nets that the class generated. Repeat the questions asked in the preceding Explore section.

- *What is the total area needed to cover a unit cube?*

You may want to use ACE Exercise 32 as an in-class wrap-up problem.

Materials
- Student notebook

ACE Assignment Guide for Problem 1.1

Core 1–3, 16
Other *Applications* 4, *Connections* 15, 17–18; *Extensions* 32

Adapted For suggestions about adapting ACE exercises, see the CMP *Special Needs Handbook*.
Connecting to Prior Units 15, 18: *Covering and Surrounding*

Answers to Problem 1.1

A. There are 35 different nets that can be made with six squares (these are called hexominos). However, only the 11 shown below will fold into a cubic box. (These are shown on Transparency 1.1B.)

B. The area of each net is 6 square units. A unit cube has 6 faces, each of which has an area of 1 square unit.

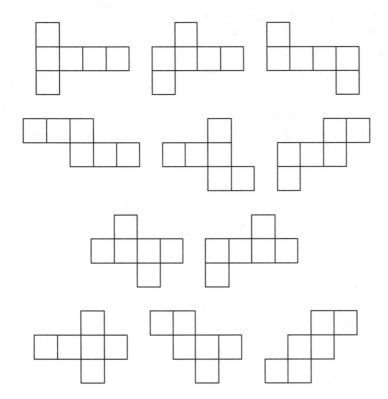

Goals

- Visualize a net as a representation of the surface area of a rectangular prism

- Connect the area of the net to the surface area of a rectangular prism

In this problem, students design nets for a rectangular box.

Launch 1.2

Hold up a rectangular box that is not a cube and ask students to describe it. Discuss the features of the box—faces, edges, and vertices.

Suggested Questions Ask:

- *Describe the faces of this rectangular box.* (They are rectangles, and opposite faces are congruent.)

- *How many faces are there?* (6)

- *How many edges does the box have?* (12)

- *How many vertices does it have?* (8)

- *Will a different box have a different number of faces, edges, or vertices?*

Hold up a different box. Make sure the class realizes that, like cubes, all rectangular prisms have 6 faces, 12 edges, and 8 vertices. You may introduce the term *rectangular prism* now or wait until Problem 1.3 where it is introduced in the text.

Explain that packaging engineers may design a rectangular box by drawing a net that can be cut out and folded to make the box. Explain that the challenge is for students to find nets that will fold to form the given box.

You may want to check that students understand how to find the area of a rectangle. (If they have not worked through the *Covering and Surrounding* unit, you may want to review briefly the concepts of area and perimeter.)

Distribute centimeter grid paper. Have students investigate the problem on their own and then compare results in groups of 2 or 3.

Explore 1.2

Once students have drawn two nets and answered the questions about them, they should gather in their groups to compare their nets and validate that each could be folded into the same rectangular box.

As you circulate, continue to ask questions like those you asked in Problem 1.1. Ask students to show that their nets will work; to look for things that are the same in all of the nets; to look for things that are different; and to consider how the area of each net is related to the number of squares that would cover the rectangular box.

Summarize 1.2

Give students a chance to share their nets and show that they form the correct box. You might want to designate an area on the wall or chalkboard for the variety of nets to be displayed.

Suggested Questions Ask students how they found the area of their nets. The relationship between the area of the net and the surface area of the related box should be a focus of the discussion.

- *What was the area of your net?* (14 sq. cm)

- *How did you find that measure?* (Examples: Counting. I had one big rectangle, whose area was 12 sq. cm, and then I added on the two ends to get 14 sq. cm.)

- *What do you think the total area of the box's surface will be? Why?*

- *How do these areas compare?* (They are the same.) *Why does it make sense that these two measures are the same?*

You want to be sure to help students make the connection between the box's surface area and the area of plane figures. This is difficult for some students. You will want to revisit the idea explicitly in later problems.

In Question D, you might introduce the upcoming vocabulary of *volume*. This language is not essential at this point, but the idea is important.

- *What strategies did you use to find the number of unit cubes needed to fill the box?*

At some point in the discussion, you will want to demonstrate (or have students demonstrate) this filling. Use three cubes, with the same dimensions as the grid paper students are using, to demonstrate how they fill the rectangular boxes. If three cubes are needed to fill a box, the box has a volume of 3 unit cubes (or 3 cubic units).

Introduce the *dimensions* of a rectangular box: length, width, and height. First, the base of the box must be defined. The length and width of the base are two of the dimensions; the height of the box is the third. Make sure students are aware that placing the box on a different face changes the base: the face on the bottom will be called the base.

Check for Understanding

Give students the dimensions of a new box (preferably one you can display in front of the class) and ask them to sketch each face, labeling the dimensions and area of each face. It is best at this time to use a box with whole-number dimensions to demonstrate this.

This summary can help launch the next problem.

1.2 Making Rectangular Boxes

Mathematical Goals

- Visualize a net as a representation of the surface area of a rectangular prism
- Connect the area of the net to the surface area of a rectangular prism

Launch

Hold up a rectangular box that is not a cube and ask students to describe it. Discuss the features of the box.

- *Describe the faces of this rectangular box. How many faces are there?*
- *How many edges does the box have?*
- *How many vertices does it have?*
- *Will a different box have a different number of faces, edges, or vertices?*

Hold up a different box.

Explain that packaging engineers may design a rectangular box by drawing a net that can be cut out and folded to make the box. Explain the challenge for students.

Have students work on their own, then compare results in pairs or threes.

Materials

- cm grid paper
- cm cubes (optional)
- Scissors
- 2 or 3 rectangular boxes

Vocabulary

- Dimensions

Explore

Once students have drawn two nets and answered the questions about them, they should gather in their groups to compare their nets and validate that each could be folded into the same rectangular box.

Continue to ask questions like those you asked in Problem 1.1. Ask students to show that their nets will work; to look for things that are the same in all of the nets; to look for things that are different; and to consider how the area of each net is related to the number of squares that would cover the rectangular box.

Summarize

Give students a chance to share and display their nets. Ask students how they found the area of their nets. The relationship between the area of the net and the surface area of the related box should be a focus of the discussion.

- *What was the area of your net?*
- *How did you find that measure?*
- *What do you think the total area of the box's surface will be? Why?*
- *How do these areas compare?*
- *Why does it make sense that these two measures are the same?*

Materials

- Student notebook

continued on next page

Help students make the connection between the box's surface area and the area of plane figures.

- *What strategies did you use to find the number of unit cubes needed to fill the box?*

Demonstrate this filling. Use three cubes to demonstrate how they fill the rectangular boxes. Introduce the *dimensions* of a rectangular box: length, width, and height. Make sure students are aware that placing the box on a different face changes the base.

Give students the dimensions of a new box and ask them to sketch each face, labeling the dimensions and area of each face.

ACE Assignment Guide for Problem 1.2

Core 5–7

Other *Connections* 19–24; unassigned choices from previous problems

Adapted For suggestions about adapting ACE exercises, see the CMP *Special Needs Handbook.* **Connecting to Prior Units** 19–22: *Covering and Surrounding*

Answers to Problem 1.2

A. Possible nets:

B. Four rectangular faces are congruent, with a length of 3 cm and a width of 1 cm. The remaining two faces are also congruent, with a length of 1 cm and a width of 1 cm.

C. The area for each net in Question A is 14 cm^2.

D. 3 cm cubes. One cube will cover the square end and fill one third of the box, so two more will fill the box.

E. No. If the position of the box is changed, the area of a net for the box and number of cubes needed to fill the box remain the same.

1.3 Testing Nets

Goals

- Visualize a net as a representation of the surface area of a rectangular prism
- Use a net for a rectangular prism to develop a strategy for finding the surface area of the prism
- Find the volume of a rectangular prism by counting the number of unit cubes it takes to fill the prism

In this problem, students make boxes from nets. The area of a net is the surface area of the related box—the amount of packaging material needed to wrap, or cover, the box. After making the boxes, students fill them with centimeter cubes to find their volumes.

Launch 1.3

Launch the problem with the Getting Ready. You might want to use an example of a rectangular prism with dimensions 2 cm by 5 cm by 8 cm.

Suggested Questions Ask:

- *What are the dimensions of each face?*
- *What patterns do you observe among the faces?*
- *What are the dimensions of the prism?*

Turn the prism to rest on another face.

- *What are the dimensions?*

To make a net out of the box; students may suggest cutting the edge labeled length, the 4 edges forming the height of the box, and the two edges in the base of the box that signify the width. There are different choices of edges to cut that would make the box fold flat to form a net.

Tell the story of the engineer who has lost his notes indicating the dimensions of each box. Distribute Labsheet 1.3 to each student.

Suggested Questions Before students begin cutting out the nets, ask:

- *Make a guess and record the dimensions of each box.* (This will help strengthen their visualization skills and understanding of dimensions.)

Students can work in groups of 2–3.

Explore 1.3

Before cutting it out, ask students to draw in the fold lines for each net. Then have them shade in one of each of the three different size faces of the box on the net. Ask how this helps find the dimensions of the box.

In Question B, if students are having difficulties finding the dimensions, have them cut out the nets and then find the dimensions and the number of unit cubes needed to fill each box. Have students fold the nets with the squares on the outside of the box so that they can check their work.

If students are having trouble finding the surface area in Question C once the net is folded, have them unfold the box to find the surface area. Students can also use an extra copy of Labsheet 1.3 for this purpose. You might want to ask some students to cut out their nets in Question E to share during the summary.

Summarize 1.3

Suggested Questions Ask students:

- *Explain how you decided where to fold each net.* (Some will have used the symmetry of the two pieces that "stick out" as the place to begin folding.)
- *What are the dimensions of each box?*
- *How can you find the dimensions from the nets? From the box? How are they related?* (Stress the importance of the base, its dimensions, and the height—the distance from the base to the top of the box.)
- *What features of the box do you observe that might make it easier to find the surface area?* (Emphasize that the faces of a box come in pairs—this will be an important idea when students develop strategies for finding surface area.)

When discussing the number of unit cubes needed to fill each box, do not go for rules—it is the filling idea that is important at this stage of students' development of the concept of volume. Some students may have already found effective ways to count the cubes—for example, by multiplying the number of cubes needed to fill the bottom of the box by the number of layers of cubes needed to fill the entire box. You could put these on the blackboard as a conjecture and come back to it. The rule or formula for finding surface area and volume will be developed in the next investigation.

Have students share their solutions to Question C. As each student displays his or her net and tells the class its dimensions and its area, ask the class whether they agree that the net works.

For Question E, put up several different nets. You may want to record the dimensions of each net, surface area, and volume in a table on poster paper.

Suggested Questions This will be useful for Investigation 2. Ask:

- *How does your new net, its dimensions, and its area compare to those for Box P?*

- *Do any of these nets have non-square faces? If not, draw a net that would have all non-square faces. (for example: 4 × 0.5 × 3)*

1.3 Testing Nets

Mathematical Goals

- Visualize a net as a representation of the surface area of a rectangular prism
- Use a net for a rectangular prism to develop a strategy for finding the surface area of the prism
- Find the volume of a rectangular prism by counting the number of unit cubes it takes to fill the prism

Launch

Tell the story of the engineer who has lost his notes indicating the dimensions of each box. Distribute Labsheet 1.3 to each student. Before students begin cutting out the nets, ask them to guess and record the dimensions of each box. This will help strengthen their visualization skills. Students can work in groups of 2–3.

Materials
- Transparencies 1.3A and 1.3B
- Labsheet 1.3
- Scissors
- cm cubes

Vocabulary
- rectangular prism
- base

Explore

Have students cut out the nets and then find the dimensions and the number of unit cubes needed to fill each box. Have students fold the nets so the squares are on the outside of the box.

You might want to ask some students to cut out their nets in Question E to share during the summary.

Summarize

Ask students to explain how they decided where to fold each net. Some will have used the symmetry of the two pieces that "stick out" as the place to begin folding.

Discuss the dimensions of each box. Emphasize that the faces of a box come in pairs—this will be an important idea when students develop strategies for finding surface area. Stress the importance of the base, its dimensions, and the height (the distance from the base to the top of the box).

When discussing the number of unit cubes needed to fill each box, do not go for rules. The rule or formula for finding surface area and volume will be developed in the next investigation.

Have students share their solutions to Question C. As each student displays his or her net and tells the class its dimensions and its area, ask the class whether they agree that the net works. Also ask how the net, its dimensions, and its area compare to those for Box P.

Materials
- Student notebooks

ACE Assignment Guide for Problem 1.3

Core 8–9
Other *Connections* 25–27, 31

Adapted For suggestions about adapting Exercise 7 and other ACE exercises, see the CMP *Special Needs Handbook*.
Connecting to Prior Units 25, 26: *Covering and Surrounding*; 27: *Bits and Pieces II*; 31: *Bits and Pieces III*

Answers to Problem 1.3

A.

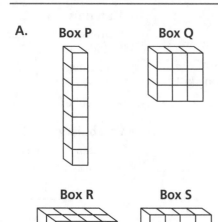

Box P: 1 cm by 1 cm by 6 cm;
Box Q: 1 cm by 3 cm by 3 cm;
Box R: 2 cm by 2 cm by 4 cm;
Box S: 1 cm by 4 cm by 4 cm.

B. Each combination of two dimensions will yield the dimensions for a pair of congruent faces.

C. Box P: 26 cm^2; Box Q: 30 cm^2; Box R: 40 cm^2; Box S: 48 cm^2.

D. Box P: 6 unit cubes; Box Q: 9 unit cubes; Box R: 16 unit cubes; Box S: 16 unit cubes.

E. Answers will vary. The box should hold 6 unit cubes and have dimensions 1 cm by 2 cm by 3 cm.

Flattening a Box

Goals

- Understand the relationship between the dimensions of a rectangular prism and its surface area

- Calculate the surface area of a rectangular prism

- Continue to develop visualization skills relating rectangular prisms to their nets

Students find the dimensions of a box, then design a net that will fold into a box with those dimensions.

You will need a small box (such as a jewelry box, small gift box, or individual cereal box) for each pair of students. It might make the discussion easier if you used the same box, such as the individual cereal boxes, or if you use boxes with "nice numbers" for dimensions and provide a few extras for challenges. If you cannot find boxes with fairly easy numbers to work with, you could direct students to round dimensions down to whole numbers. You could have a few different sizes to give to students who finish the Explore early. If you cannot find enough small boxes, tell the students with larger boxes that each unit on the grid paper corresponds to a particular length on the real box—for example, 1 centimeter on the grid paper might correspond to 5 centimeters on the real box.

The various boxes you have collected may have open tops or tops that overlap. Decide whether you want students to cut out a net that will produce a closed-top or an open-top version of each box. In the past, teachers have had success with paper clip boxes, single-serving cereal boxes, and juice boxes. Some boxes have flaps. At this point a good strategy is to tell the class to ignore them for the net.

Some teachers find it convenient to give each student (or pair of students) an identical box so that the nets and measurements can be compared to each other. Others limit the choice to 2 or 3 identical boxes so that there is some variety in shapes in the summary. Yet other teachers use a large variety of boxes. Any of these choices is fine.

Demonstrate the relationship of the dimensions of a box to the dimensions of its faces. Hold up one of the boxes.

Suggested Questions Ask:

- *Can you estimate the length, width, and height of this box?*

- *How can we determine these dimensions?* (We can measure them.)

- *What would a net for this box look like?*

Students should realize that all 6 faces (5 if they are making nets for open boxes) will be represented in some way in the net.

Make one of the measurements in centimeters and talk about the fact that it may not be a whole number. Take a moment to discuss how accurately you want students to measure; tenths of centimeters (i.e., millimeters) should be sufficient.

Pairs can work together to measure the faces of their box, but each student should design a net for the box.

Distribute centimeter grid paper and one box to each pair of students. Students can exchange and then test their nets to verify that they fold into a box the same size as the one you have given them.

Some students may need help getting started. Some may need to begin with sketching the individual faces and then assembling them on grid paper to make a connected net.

Going Further Ask some students to design a net for a box with flaps.

INVESTIGATION 1

Suggested Questions Let some pairs summarize their work and any problems they ran into.

- *What strategy did you use? What difficulties did you encounter?* (The easiest strategy for finding a net that works is to think about cutting along the vertical edges and laying the faces of the box flat. Be sure to look for other ways students reasoned about designing a net.)

- *Why might the area of the faces of a box be important?* (Talk about the area of the faces of a box and why this might be an important measurement for a packaging engineer.)

Hold up one of the boxes and turn it so that one of the lateral sides is the base, and then ask:

- *What if the base of the box is this face; how would it affect the dimensions? The surface area?*

You might ask students how many unit cubes will fit into their boxes. If the dimensions of their boxes are not whole numbers, this will require some estimation. Don't talk about rules for finding volume yet; at this point, it is simply the idea of filling that is important.

Check for Understanding

If the length, width, and height of a rectangular box are 3 cm, 5 cm, and 10 cm, respectively, what is the surface area of the box?

1.4 Flattening a Box

Mathematical Goals

- Understand the relationship between the dimensions of a rectangular prism and its surface area
- Calculate the surface area of a rectangular prism
- Continue to develop visualization skills relating rectangular prisms to their nets

Launch

Demonstrate the relationship of the dimensions of a box to the dimensions of its faces. Hold up one of the boxes.

- *Can you estimate the length, width, and height of this box?*
- *How can we determine these dimensions? What would a net for this box look like?*

Students should realize that all six faces will be represented in some way in the net.

Talk about the fact that not all measurements will be whole numbers. Discuss how accurately you want students to measure; tenths of centimeters (i.e., millimeters) should be sufficient.

Pairs can work together to measure the faces of their box, but each student should design a net for the box.

Materials
- Rectangular box

Explore

Distribute centimeter grid paper and one box to each pair of students. They can exchange and then test their nets to verify that they fold into a box the same size as the one you have given them.

If some students still can't find the net, then suggest that they do Question C before Question B.

Materials
- Small rectangular boxes (1 per pair)
- Scissors
- Rulers
- Tape
- cm grid paper

Summarize

Let each pair summarize their work and any problems they ran into. The easiest strategy for finding a net that works is to think about cutting along the vertical edges and laying the faces of the box flat. Be sure to look for other ways students reasoned about designing a net.

Talk about the area of the faces of a box and why this might be an important measurement for a packaging engineer.

Materials
- Student notebooks

continued on next page

You might ask students how many unit cubes will fit into their boxes. If the dimensions of their boxes are not whole numbers, this will require some estimation. Don't talk about rules for finding volume yet; at this point, it is simply the idea of filling that is important.

Check for Understanding

If the length, width, and height of a rectangular box are 3 cm, 5 cm, and 10 cm, respectively, what is the surface area of the box?

ACE Assignment Guide for Problem 1.4

Differentiated Instruction
Solutions for All Learners

Core 10–13
Other *Applications* 14, *Connections* 28–30, *Extensions* 33; and unassigned choices from previous problems
Adapted For suggestions about adapting ACE exercises, see the CMP *Special Needs Handbook*.
Connecting to Prior Units 28, 29: *Bits and Pieces II*; 30: *Bits and Pieces III*

Answers to Problem 1.4

Answers will vary for all of parts A–D. The answers given are based on a box for staples, pictured below:

A. length 11 cm, width 4 cm, height 2.5 cm

B. Possible net:

C. Cut along the dark lines to make the net in B.

D. The area of the net above is 163 cm^2. This comes to 16.3¢ per box.

This would be useful if Amy were trying to decide among two or more different box designs. Cost might be one of the factors she considers. It also might be useful if she is trying to decide how much to charge for the product in the box.

E. Students may suggest such possibilities as the area of the front of the box for logos and decoration, the location of the *top* of the box, and the thickness of the cardboard.

Investigation 1

Building Boxes

The most common type of package is the rectangular box. Rectangular boxes contain everything from cereal to shoes and from pizza to paper clips. Most rectangular boxes begin as flat sheets of cardboard, which are cut and then folded into a box shape.

1.1 Making Cubic Boxes

Some boxes are shaped like cubes. A **cube** is a three-dimensional shape with six identical square faces.

What kinds of things might be packaged in cubic boxes?

The boxes you will work with in this problem are shaped like unit cubes. A **unit cube** is a cube with edges that are 1 unit long. For example, cubes that are 1 inch on each edge are called inch cubes. Cubes that are 1 centimeter on each edge are called centimeter cubes.

In this problem, you will make nets that can be folded to form boxes. A **net** is a two-dimensional pattern that can be folded to form a three-dimensional figure. The diagram below shows one possible net for a cubic box.

Investigation 1 Building Boxes **5**

Notes _____

_____

_____

_____

Problem 1.1 Making Cubic Boxes

On grid paper, draw nets that can be folded to make a unit cube.

A. How many different nets can you make that will fold into a box shaped like a unit cube?

B. What is the total area of each net, in square units?

ACE Homework starts on page 10.

1.2 Making Rectangular Boxes

Many boxes are not shaped like cubes. The rectangular box below has square ends, but the remaining faces are non-square rectangles.

1 cm
1 cm
3 cm

Problem 1.2 Making Rectangular Boxes

A. On grid paper, draw two different nets for the rectangular box above. Cut each pattern out and fold it into a box.

B. Describe the faces of the box formed from each net you made. What are the dimensions of each face?

C. Find the total area of each net you made in Question A.

D. How many centimeter cubes will fit into the box formed from each net you made? Explain your reasoning.

E. Suppose you stand the rectangular 1 centimeter × 1 centimeter × 3 centimeters box on its end. Does the area of a net for the box or the number of cubes needed to fill the box change?

ACE Homework starts on page 10.

active math online

For: Virtual Box Activity
Visit: PHSchool.com
Web Code: and-6102

Notes _____

_____

_____

_____

1.3 Testing Nets

All the boxes you have made so far are rectangular prisms. A **rectangular prism** is a three-dimensional shape with six rectangular faces. The size of a rectangular prism can be described by giving its *dimensions*. The dimensions are the length, the width, and the height.

The **base** of a rectangular prism is the face on the bottom (the face that rests on the table or floor). The length and width of a prism are the length and width of its rectangular base. The height is the distance from the base of the prism to its top.

Getting Ready for Problem 1.3

- Suppose you want to cut the box in the figure below to make a net for the box. Along which edges can you make the cut?

- Are there different choices of edges to cut that will work?

Notes _____

_____

_____

_____

An engineer at the Save-a-Tree packaging company drew the nets below. He lost the notes that indicated the dimensions of the boxes. Use your thinking from the Getting Ready section to work backwards and determine the dimensions for him.

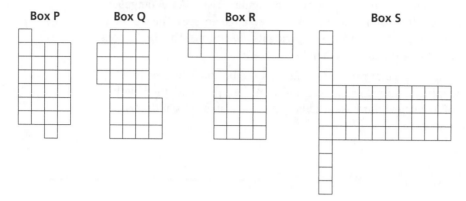

Box P   Box Q   Box R   Box S

Problem 1.3 Rectangular Prisms

A. Using a copy of the diagram above, draw in fold lines and cut each pattern and fold it to form a box. What are the dimensions of each box?

B. How are the dimensions of each box related to the dimensions of its faces?

C. What is the total area, in square units, of all the faces of each box?

D. Fill each box with unit cubes. How many unit cubes does it take to fill each box?

E. Design a net for a box that has a different shape than Box P but holds the same number of cubes as Box P.

 ACE Homework starts on page 10.

1.4 Flattening a Box

Amy is a packaging engineer at the Save-a-Tree packaging company. Mr. Shu asks Amy to come to his class and explain her job to his students. She gives each student a box to do some exploring.

8 Filling and Wrapping

Notes _____

_____

_____

_____

Problem 1.4 Surface Area of a Rectangular Prism

Your teacher will give you a box.

A. Find the dimensions of the box.

B. Use the dimensions of the box to make a net on centimeter grid paper. You may find it helpful to put the box on the paper, outline the base, and then roll the box over so a new face touches the paper.

C. Match each face of the box to your net in Question B. Label the net to show how the faces match.

D. Amy explained that one thing she considers when designing a box is the cost of the material. Suppose the material for the box costs $\frac{1}{10}$ of a cent per square centimeter. What is the total cost of the material for the box? Why might this information be useful?

E. What other information do you think is important to consider when designing a box?

ACE Homework starts on page 10.

Did You Know?

It is possible to receive a college degree in packaging. A packaging degree prepares a person to develop and produce packages for a variety of products. The designer must pay attention to cost, durability, transportability, safety and environmental regulations, and visual appeal. Many manufacturing companies want people with packaging degrees. However, there are only a few colleges or universities that offer a bachelor's degree in packaging.

Go Online
PHSchool.com
For: Information about a degree in packaging
Web Code: ane-9031

Investigation 1 Building Boxes **9**

Notes _____
_____
_____
_____

Applications

For Exercises 1–4, decide if you can fold the net along the lines to form a closed cubic box. If you are unsure, draw the pattern on grid paper and cut it out to experiment.

1.
2.
3.
4.

5. Which of these nets could be folded along the lines to form a closed rectangular box?

A.
B.
C.

6. Do parts (a)–(c) for each pattern from Exercise 5 that forms a closed rectangular box.

   a. Use the unit square shown to help you find the dimensions of the box.

unit square

   b. Find the total area, in square units, of all the faces of the box.

   c. Find the number of unit cubes it would take to fill the box.

10   Filling and Wrapping

Notes _____

_____

_____

_____

7. This closed rectangular box does not have square ends.

2 cm

1 cm

4 cm

a. What are the dimensions of the box?

b. On centimeter grid paper, sketch two nets for the box.

c. Find the area, in square centimeters, of each net.

d. Find the total area of all the faces of the box. How does your answer compare with the areas you found in part (c)?

8. Which of these patterns can be folded along the lines to form a closed rectangular box? Explain.

a.

b.

c.

d.

e.

Investigation 1 Building Boxes   **11**

Notes _____

_____

_____

_____

9. Can you fold this net along the lines to form an open cubic box? Explain your reasoning.

For each box described in Exercises 10–13:

- Make a sketch of the box and label the dimensions.
- Draw a net.
- Find the area of each face.
- Find the total area of all the faces.

10. a rectangular box with dimensions 2 centimeters × 3 centimeters × 5 centimeters

11. a rectangular box with dimensions $2\frac{1}{2}$ centimeters × 2 centimeters × 1 centimeter

12. a cubic box with side lengths $3\frac{2}{3}$ centimeters

13. a cubic box that holds 125 unit cubes

Homework Help Online
PHSchool.com
For: Help with Exercise 10
Web Code: ane-6110

14. An open box is a box without a top.

a. On grid paper, sketch nets for three different open cubic boxes.

b. On grid paper, sketch nets for three different open rectangular boxes (not cubic boxes) with square ends.

c. Find the area of each net you found in parts (a) and (b).

Notes _____

_____

_____

_____

Connections

For Exercises 15–18, use the following information: A *hexomino* is a shape made of six identical squares connected along their sides. The nets for a closed cubic box are examples of hexominos. Below are five different hexominos.

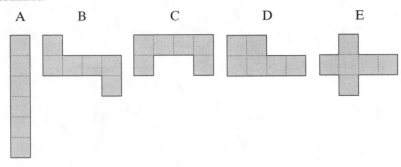

A   B   C   D   E

15. Find the perimeter of each hexomino shown above.

16. Which hexominos can you fold to form a closed cubic box?

17. From which hexominos can you remove one square to make a net for an open cubic box? For each hexomino you select, draw a diagram showing which square can be removed.

18. To which hexominos can you add the number of squares below without changing the perimeter? For each hexomino you select, draw a diagram. Explain why the perimeter does not change.

    a. one square   **b.** two squares

Investigation 1 Building Boxes   **13**

Notes _____

_____

_____

_____

For Exercises 19–22, find the area and the perimeter of each figure. Figures are not drawn to scale.

Go Online
PHSchool.com
For: Multiple-Choice Skills Practice
Web Code: ana-6154

19.

4 cm

5 cm

4 cm

7 cm

20.

6 cm

21.

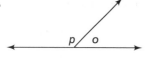

9 cm

10 cm

8.74 cm

7 cm

22.

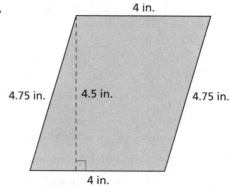

4 in.

4.75 in.   4.5 in.   4.75 in.

4 in.

23. Which pair of angles are complementary angles?

a.

p   o

b.

r
q

c.

s   t

24. Angles *m* and *n* below are supplementary angles. Angle *m* has a measure of 78°. What is the measure of angle *n*?

m   n

Notes _____

_____

_____

_____

25. Multiple Choice Which angle is supplementary to a 57° angle?

A. 123° B. 57° C. 33° D.

26. What measurements do you need and how do you use those measurements to find the area and perimeter of each figure below?

    a. rectangle   **b.** square

27. Mrs. Zhou is making wooden slats for doll beds from a strip of thin board.

She cuts $\frac{1}{12}$ of the strip for another project. Bed slats for one doll bed take $\frac{1}{8}$ of a strip.

$\frac{1}{12}$

    a. Suppose Mrs. Zhou uses the remainder of this strip for bed slats. How many doll beds can she make?

    b. Draw diagrams to confirm your answer.

Notes _____

_____

_____

_____

28. a. Four friends shared $\frac{3}{5}$ of a pizza. What fraction of the pizza did each receive?

b. Draw a picture to confirm your answer.

29. Mr. Bouck is making snack bars. The recipe calls for $\frac{3}{8}$ stick of butter. He has $3\frac{1}{2}$ sticks on hand.

a. How many recipes can he make?

b. Draw a picture to show your reasoning.

30. Tom plans to plant an herb garden in a glass tank. A scoop of dirt fills 0.15 of the volume of the tank. He needs to put in dirt equal to 65% of the volume. How many scoops of dirt does he need?

0.15 of volume

Notes _____

_____

_____

_____

31. A glass container is 0.5 full of water. After 400 milliliters are poured out, the container is 0.34 full. How much does the container hold?

Extensions

32. A number cube is designed so that numbers on opposite sides add to 7. Write the integers from 1 to 6 on one of the nets you found in Problem 1.1 so that it can be folded to form this number cube. You may want to test your pattern by cutting it out and folding it.

33. Examine the nets you made for cubic boxes in Problem 1.1. Suppose you want to make boxes by tracing several copies of the same pattern onto a large sheet of cardboard and cutting them out.

Which pattern allows you to make the greatest number of boxes from a square sheet of cardboard with a side length of 10 units? Test your ideas on grid paper.

Investigation 1 Building Boxes   **17**

Notes _____

_____

_____

_____

Mathematical Reflections 1

In this investigation, you explored rectangular boxes, and you made nets for boxes. You found the dimensions of a box, the total area of all its faces, and the number of unit cubes required to fill it. These questions will help you summarize what you have learned.

Think about your answers to these questions. Discuss your ideas with other students and your teacher. Then write a summary of your findings in your notebook.

1. Explain how to find the total area of all the faces of a rectangular box.

2. Explain how to find the number of identical cubes it will take to fill a rectangular box.

3. Suppose several different nets are made for a given box. What do all of the nets have in common? What might be different?

18 Filling and Wrapping

Notes _____

_____

_____

_____

Investigation 1

ACE
Assignment Choices

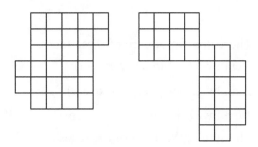
Differentiated Instruction
Solutions for All Learners

Problem 1.1
Core 1–3, 16
Other *Applications* 4, *Connections* 15, 17–18;
Extensions 32

Problem 1.2
Core 5–7
Other *Connections* 19–24; and unassigned choices
from previous problems

Problem 1.3
Core 8–9
Other *Connections* 25–27, 31; and unassigned
choices from previous problems

Problem 1.4
Core 10–13
Other *Applications* 14, *Connections* 28–30,
Extensions 33; and unassigned choices from
previous problems

Adapted For suggestions about adapting
Exercise 7 and other ACE exercises, see the
CMP *Special Needs Handbook*.
Connecting to Prior Units 15, 18–22, 26: *Covering
and Surrounding*; 27–29: *Bits and Pieces II*; 30, 31:
Bits and Pieces III

Applications

1-4. Patterns 2 and 4 *do* form closed boxes.
Patterns 1 and 3 *do not*.

5. Patterns A and B *can* be folded to form a
closed box. Pattern C *cannot*.

6. a. Pattern A: 1 unit by 1 unit by 4 units
Pattern B: 1 unit by 2 units by 4 units

 b. Pattern A: 18 sq. units
Pattern B: 28 sq. units

 c. Pattern A: 4 cubes
Pattern B: 8 cubes

7. a. 2 cm by 4 cm by 1 cm
 b. Possible answers:

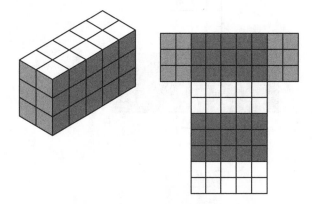

 c. All nets for this box have an area of
28 sq. cm.

 d. There are two faces with area of 8 sq. cm,
two with area 2 sq. cm, and two with area
4 sq. cm, for a total of 28 sq. cm. This is the
same as the area of the net.

8. a, c, d, and e *will not* fold into a box. b *will*.

9. This net *will* fold into an open cubic box. The
two triangles will meet to become one end of
the box

10. Sketch of box and possible net:

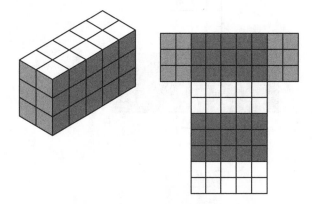

There are two of each of these faces:
2 cm by 3 cm (area is 6 sq. cm);
2 cm by 5 cm (area is 10 sq. cm);
3 cm by 5 cm (area is 15 sq. cm.).
The sum of the areas of the faces is
62 sq. cm.

11. Sketch of box and possible net:

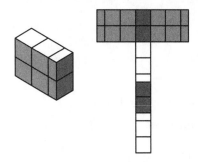

There are two of each of these faces:

2 cm by 1 cm (area is 2 sq. cm);

2 cm by $2\frac{1}{2}$ cm (area is 5 sq. cm);

1 cm by $2\frac{1}{2}$ cm (area is $2\frac{1}{2}$ sq. cm).

The sum of the areas of the faces is 19 sq. cm.

12. Sketch of box and possible net:

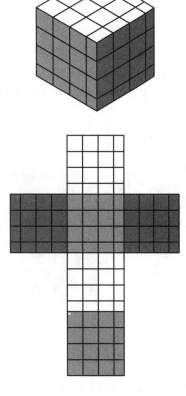

There are six faces. Each is $3\frac{2}{3}$ cm by $3\frac{2}{3}$ cm (each face has area $13\frac{4}{9}$ sq. cm).

The sum of the areas of the faces is $80\frac{2}{3}$ sq. cm.

13. Sketch of box and possible net:

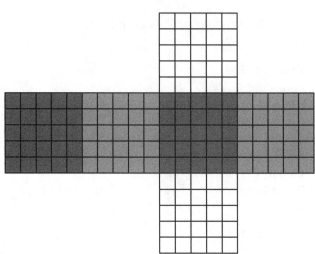

There are six faces. Each is 5 cm by 5 cm (area is 25 sq. cm).

The sum of the areas of the faces is 150 sq. cm.

14. a. Possible nets:

b. Possible nets:

c. Answers will depend on answers to parts (a) and (b). For the examples given above, the areas (in order) are: 45 sq. units, 20 sq. units, 5 sq. units, 8 sq. units, 13 sq. units, and 36 sq. units.

Connections

15. A, B, C, and E all have perimeter 14 units; D has perimeter 12 units.

16. Hexominos B and E can be folded to form a closed, cubic box.

17. Any of hexominos B, C, D, or E can have one square removed to form a net for an open cubic box. Examples:

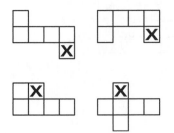

18. a. Hexominos B, C, D, and E can all have one square added while maintaining the same perimeter. The perimeter does not change if we tuck the new square into a corner—the square covers two units of perimeter while adding two new units. Example at right (the shaded square has been added in each case):

b. Hexominos B, D, and E can have two squares added while maintaining the same perimeter. Examples below:

19. area = 22 cm^2
perimeter = 20 cm

20. area $\approx$ 28.27 cm^2
perimeter $\approx$ 18.85 cm

21. area = 30.59 cm^2
perimeter = 26 cm

22. area = 18 in.^{2}
perimeter = 17.5 in.

23. b, $\angle r$ and $\angle q$ **24.** n measures 102°

25. A

26. a. To find the area and perimeter of a rectangle, you need to know the length and the width. (In fact, if we consider the set of area, perimeter, length, and width, knowing any two is sufficient information for finding the other two.) To find the area, multiply length by width. To find perimeter, add the length and width, then double the result. An alternate way to find perimeter is to double the length, double the width, and add these two results.

b. Since, in a square, length and width are equal, you need only to know the length of a side. To find the area, multiply the side length by itself. To find the perimeter, multiply the side length by four.

27. a. $\frac{11}{12} \div \frac{1}{8} = 7\frac{1}{3}$. Ms. Zhou can make slats for 7 doll beds and have enough left (if it is usable) for $\frac{1}{3}$ of another bed.

b. (Figure 1)

28. a. $\frac{3}{5} \div 4 = \frac{3}{5} \times \frac{1}{4} = \frac{3}{20}$. Each gets $\frac{3}{20}$ of the pie.

b.

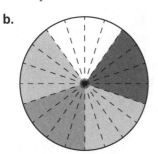

29. a. $3\frac{1}{2} \div \frac{3}{8} = \frac{28}{8} \div \frac{3}{8} = 28 \div 3 = 9\frac{1}{3}$ recipes

b. (Figure 2)

30. $0.65 \div 0.15 = 4.33$ scoops.

31. 2,500 ml

$$0.16\,c = 400 \text{ ml}$$
$$c = 400 \div 0.16$$
$$c = 2,500 \text{ ml}$$

Extensions

32. Possible answer:

	2		
1	3	6	4
	5		

33. Several shapes will allow 12 boxes to be made (for example, Figure 3 below). At least one shape will allow 13 boxes (for example, Figure 4 below).

Figure 3

Figure 4

Figure 1

Figure 2

Possible Answers to Mathematical Reflections

1. The faces of a rectangular box are rectangles. You just need to find the area of each rectangular face and add these areas. Because every box has three matching pairs of faces, you could find the area of the three different faces and then double this total.

2. You can find the number of cubes it would take to fill a box by putting the cubes inside the box and counting how many fit. If the cubes do not fit exactly, you have to estimate the partial cubes that are needed. Some students may begin to see a rule, but do not push for it at this point.

3. The number of square units in the net must be the same. The arrangement of the square units can be different, as can be the perimeter of the net. (Note: Students may have other observations. You might want to discuss students' reflections and test their ideas by examining some of the nets from this investigation.)

Investigation 2 Designing Rectangular Boxes

Mathematical and Problem-Solving Goals

- Connect the dimensions of a rectangular prism to its volume and surface area

- Understand that rectangular prisms may have the same volume but quite different surface areas

- Predict which rectangular prism of those with a common volume will have the smallest surface area

- Refine a strategy for finding the surface area of a rectangular prism

- Understand that prisms can be filled systematically in identical layers, and that this layering leads to the formula for volume

- Develop a formula for finding the volume of a rectangular prism

Summary of Problems

Problem 2.1 Packaging Blocks

Students consider rectangular prisms with a common volume of 24 in.^{3}.

Problem 2.2 Saving Trees

Students make conjectures about minimizing surface areas for rectangular prisms and are encouraged to formulate a general strategy for finding the surface area of a rectangular prism.

Problem 2.3 Filling Rectangular Boxes

By thinking about filling boxes in layers, students develop the formula for volume of a rectangular prism.

	Suggested Pacing	Materials for Students	Materials for Teachers	ACE Assignments
All	4 days			
2.1	$1\frac{1}{2}$ days	Inch cubes	Transparency 2.1; nets and boxes from Investigation 1	1–3, 20–22
2.2	1 day	Inch cubes	2 or 3 rectangular or cubic boxes	4–6, 23, 24, 28
2.3	1 day	Unit cubes (optional), boxes	Transparent models of Boxes W, X, Y and Z (optional); Transparencies 2.3 A–C	7–19, 25–27, 29
MR	$\frac{1}{2}$ day			

2.1 Packaging Blocks

Goals

- Connect the dimensions of a rectangular prism to its volume and surface area

- Understand that rectangular prisms may have the same volume but quite different surface areas

In Investigation 1, students were introduced to the idea of the surface area of a rectangular box and should have begun to make connections between the surface area and the dimensions of a box. In this problem, they find all the possible rectangular arrangements of 24 blocks and the amount of material needed to package them. Students may still be focusing on the area of each face of a box, but they should be using their knowledge about finding the area of a rectangle rather than counting individual squares. As they find different arrangements for the 24 blocks, they also begin to see connections between the dimensions of the box and its volume.

You may have introduced the vocabulary of surface area and volume in Investigation 1. If not, it can be introduced in the Launch.

Launch 2.1

Use the nets and boxes from Investigation 1 to demonstrate the concepts of volume and surface area.

Suggested Questions Ask:

- *How many unit cubes fit inside of box R?* (16)

- *The word for the number of unit cubes that fill a solid is* volume. *So the volume of box R is 16 cubic units. What is the volume of box S?* (also 16)

- *So boxes R and S have the same volume. What is different about these two boxes?* (the shape, the height, the areas of their nets)

- *We saw that the area of the net was the same as the sum of the areas of the faces of the boxes. We call this sum the* surface area *of the solid. Which box has a larger surface area, R or S?* (R has a surface area of 40 sq. units; S has a surface area of 48 sq. units, so S has a larger surface area).

A net illustrates surface area in a way that students are apt to remember: to find the total surface area, we find the area of each face and add them.

Some students will struggle with the transition between the net and the box. They may need to see the net fold into the box many times and think about the relationship between the area of the net and the total area of the faces of the box each time. Be alert for these struggles in the next few problems.

Tell the story of ATC Toy Company. Before students break into groups, ask the class to suggest one arrangement of 24 blocks and discuss how they might find its surface area. If you want students to organize their data in a table (as shown in the student edition), model the process by entering the data about the chosen arrangement into a table. Or, let students decide how to organize their work to look for patterns.

You may suggest that students make sketches for only one or two of the boxes. As discussed in the Introduction to the unit, isometric dot paper may be very helpful for students in making their sketches.

Have students work in groups of two to four. Distribute unit cubes (inch cubes, if you have them) to each group.

Explore 2.1

Encourage students to organize their information in a table as suggested in the problem or in some other way that makes sense to them. They should sketch each arrangement they find and label its dimensions. Encourage students to find ways to ensure that they have found all the boxes with whole-number dimensions.

As you listen to students talk and ask them questions, encourage the use of the vocabulary: surface area and volume.

Visualizing how to sketch the boxes may be difficult for some students. One technique is to think of drawing two offset rectangles, then connecting the corners to form the box.

Summarize 2.1

Begin the summary by collecting the data students recorded in their tables. You might start with the 24-by-1-by-1 box and model collecting data in an organized manner.

Suggested Questions Ask:

- *Did anyone find a box that holds exactly 24 cubes and has an edge length of 1? What is the length of the base of this box? What is the width of the base of this box? What is the height of this box?*

- *You know this box has a volume of 24 cubic inches because that was a requirement. How much material will it take to cover this box?*

- *Did anyone find a box that holds exactly 24 cubes and has an edge length of 2? What is the length of the base of this box? What is the width of the base of this box? What is the height of this box?*

- *How much material will it take to cover this box?*

Continue with this line of questioning for edge lengths of 3, 4, 5, 6, 7, 8, 12, and 24. Asking for an edge length of 5 or 7 should give rise to a discussion about factors.

You may need to discuss suggested arrangements that are identical; for example, someone may suggest the arrangement with length 2, width 4, and height 3 and another the arrangement with length 4, width 3, and height 2. To demonstrate their equivalence, build the arrangement and set it on the three possible bases. The edges chosen to be length, width, and height are arbitrary, although it is customary to use the length and width of the base as the length and width of the rectangular box.

Students' sketches will vary, depending on which face they use as the base.

- *How did you decide which face to use for the base? Does your choice affect the surface area of the box?* (no)

Suggested Question When you have collected all the arrangements that were found, ask students to describe the patterns they see in the table.

- *Look at the table we have generated. What patterns do you notice? Explain why the patterns make sense.*

Here are some patterns students have noticed:

Classroom Dialogue Model

Patterns From the Table

Chandra: *"The volume is always 24 cubic inches."*

This is a requirement of the problem.

J.J.: *"As one dimension increases, another one decreases."*

Pedro: *"If you put more cubes in the base, the height decreases because the total is still 24."*

Cie: *"Boxes with the same three dimensions have the same volume and surface area; a 1-by-3-by-8 box and an 8-by-3-by-1 box have the same volume and surface area."*

They are really the same box oriented differently.

Ali: *"The product of the length, width, and height must equal 24, which is the volume."*

Since length times width tells how many cubes are in a layer, and height tells how many layers there are, multiplying them will give the number of cubes, or cubic inches, that will fill the box.

Some students will begin to understand that the factors of 24 are what determine the possible arrangements of 24 cubes. Some may see that volume is equal to length × width × height and use this idea to find boxes that work. If students offer the formula for finding the volume of a box, ask them to try the rule on some other boxes—for example, a box with a length of 7 units, a width of 3 units, and a height of 2 units, or a box with a length of 6 units, a width of 8 units, and a height of 1 unit. Ask them why this works. Be sure that students understand the "layering" strategy for finding volume—the number of blocks in the first layer times the number of layers or area of the base times height. Ask them to build these boxes and check to see that the pattern for finding the volume works. If students have not yet discovered this, it will surface in the next problem.

At this point, students will begin to see that, to find the surface area of a prism, they need to find the area of each of the six faces and add them. Some will see that opposite faces are equivalent and will double the area of a face to get the area of the pair.

Students may have difficulty when trying to work from the dimensions alone. For example, the surface area of a 2-by-3-by-4 box can be found from this information alone, as each pair of dimensions specifies two faces of the box (2 by 3, 2 by 4, and 3 by 4). Many students will still need to sketch or build the box or make a pattern for it to find the surface area. Asking them to notice opposite faces will move them toward a more efficient process for determining surface area.

Suggested Questions Discuss in detail which box has the least surface area (requires the least amount of material), which has the greatest, and what these boxes look like.

- *Which of the boxes with a volume of 24 cubic units has the greatest surface area?* (the 1-by-1-by-24 box)

- *What does it look like?* (long and skinny)

- *Which has the least surface area?* (the 2-by-3-by-4 box)

- *What does it look like?* (more like a cube)

- *If you were going to make a box to hold 36 cubes, which of the possible arrangements of 36 cubes would have the greatest surface area?* (a 1-by-1-by-36 arrangement, with a surface area of 146 square units)

- *Why?* (because the cubes are spread out as much as possible)

- *If you were going to make a box to hold 36 cubes, which design would cost you the least to enclose?* (a 3-by-3-by-4 arrangement, with a surface area of 66 square units)

- *Why?* (because the cubes are arranged in a more compact fashion, so more faces of the cubes are covered up)

Mathematical Goals

- Connect the dimensions of a rectangular prism to its volume and surface area
- Understand that rectangular prisms may have the same volume but quite different surface areas

Launch

Use the nets and boxes from Investigation 1 to demonstrate the concepts of volume and surface area.

- *How many unit cubes fit inside of box R?*
- *The word for the number of unit cubes that fill a solid is* volume. *What is the volume of box S?*
- *So boxes R and S have the same volume. What is different about these two boxes?*
- *We call the sum of the areas of the faces the* surface area *of the solid. Which box has a larger surface area, R or S?*

Tell the story of ATC Toy Company. Before students break into groups, have the class suggest one arrangement of 24 blocks and discuss how they might find its surface area. If you want students to organize their data in a table (as shown in the student edition), model the process by entering the data about the chosen arrangement into a table. Or, let students decide how to organize their work to look for patterns.

You may suggest that students make sketches for only one or two of the boxes.

Have students work in groups of two to four.

Materials
- Inch cubes or other unit cubes
- Transparency 2.1
- Nets and boxes from Investigation 1

Vocabulary
- volume
- surface area

Explore

Encourage students to organize their information in a table as suggested in the problem or in some other way that makes sense to them. They should sketch each arrangement they find and label its dimensions.

As you listen to students talk and ask them questions, encourage the use of the vocabulary: surface area and volume.

Summarize

Begin the summary by collecting students' data.

- *Did anyone find a box that holds exactly 24 cubes and has an edge length of 1?*
- *How much material will it take to cover this box?*
- *Did anyone find a box that holds exactly 24 cubes and has an edge length of 2?*

Continue with this line of questioning. Discuss identical arrangements.

Materials
- Student notebooks

continued on next page

- *How did you decide which face to use for the base? Does your choice affect the surface area of the box?*

Have students describe the patterns they see in the table.

Discuss which box has the least surface area, which has the greatest, and what these boxes look like.

ACE Assignment Guide for Problem 2.1

Differentiated Instruction
Solutions for All Learners

Core 1–3, 20
Other *Connections* 21, 22

Adapted For suggestions about adapting ACE exercises, see the CMP *Special Needs Handbook*.
Connecting to Prior Units 20: *Prime Time*; 22: *Variables and Patterns*

Answers to Problem 2.1

A. (Note: Students' sketches may show the same arrangement in a different orientation.)

(Figure 1)

B. The 4-by-3-by-2 box requires the least amount of material. The 24-by-1-by-1 box requires the most material.

C. Possible answer: ATC Toy Company should use the 4-by-3-by-2 box because it has the least surface area (52 in.^{2}) and would therefore be the least expensive to buy or to make. (Note: The box shaped most like a cube will always have the least surface area. This is pursued in more depth in Problem 2.2. Don't expect your class to make this generalization at this time.)

Some students may argue for boxes based on their visual appeal to the buyer.

D. Possible answer: Because 24 has more factors than 26, there are more ways to effectively package 24 blocks. With 26 blocks, you only have a 1-by-1-by-26 or a 1-by-2-by-13 arrangement. These two boxes are long and thin, so they will have larger surface areas than if the box could be more cubic in shape, like you can get with 24 blocks.

Some students might argue that the lesser-used letters don't need their own blocks, so the company can economize by making sets of 24 instead of 26.

Figure 1

Possible Arrangements of 24 Cubes

Length (in.)	Width (in.)	Height (in.)	Vol (in.^{3})	Surface areas (in.^{2})	Sketch
24	1	1	24	98	
12	2	1	24	76	
8	3	1	24	70	
6	4	1	24	68	
6	2	2	24	56	
4	3	2	24	52	

Saving Trees

Goals

- Predict which rectangular prism of those with a common volume will have the smallest surface area

- Refine a strategy for finding the surface area of a rectangular prism

This problem encourages students to find a general pattern for which rectangular arrangement of a given number of cubes will have the least surface area. The summary of Problem 2.1 leads nicely into changing the context from looking for a box that will hold exactly 24 cubes to investigating whether there is a way to find the box with minimal surface area for any fixed volume.

Launch 2.2

Review what students learned in Problem 2.1.

- *How would you describe the shape of the box we found in the last problem that held 24 cubes and had the least amount of surface area?* (The box was the one in which the dimensions were the closest, 4 by 3 by 2.)

Introduce Problem 2.2

It took a lot of work to find all the possible box arrangements for a volume of 24 cubic units. From the table we made, we found the box with the least surface area.

In mathematics, we are always looking for patterns and rules that will help us to predict outcomes. In today's problem, you are challenged to explore rectangular prisms with different volumes. You are asked to look carefully at the data and make conjectures about what you think will help you to predict the arrangement with the smallest surface area.

Let the class work on the problem in groups of 3 or 4.

Explore 2.2

Encourage groups who make conjectures about the arrangement of cubes that requires the least amount of packaging material to test other arrangements of the same number of cubes.

- *Test your conjectures on a number of cubes other than the 8, 27, and 12 suggested in the problem.*

Groups will have to find a way to organize their data, probably by using a table. If a group is having trouble with the problem, talk through the case of eight cubes with them. Ask them to build each arrangement and to look at the physical objects as well as the measures in their table.

Suggested Questions Ask:

- *Look at the dimensions for each arrangement and how they change from one arrangement to another. What is the difference between the box with the greatest surface area and the box with the least surface area?*

- *How does this difference show up in the actual boxes made from cubes?*

- *How does this difference show up in the dimensions of the boxes?*

Going Further Suppose we can fill the box with non-whole cubes (parts of cubes). How would this change your answers to Problems 2.1 and 2.2?

Summarize 2.2

Ask students to explain why the more cube-like rectangular arrangement requires the least packaging material.

Describe how you found the amount of packaging material (the surface area) required for the different arrangements you made.

- *What are the dimensions of the box with the least surface area that holds 8 cubes? The greatest surface area?*

Suggested Questions Ask the same questions for 27 cubes and 12 cubes. Display the answers to the three questions, putting the boxes with the greatest surface area together and those with the least surface area together.

- *How would you describe these shapes compared to these?* (Those with the greatest surface area are long and spread out; those with the least surface area are more compact, more like a cube.)

- *Why is the more cube-like rectangular box the box with the least surface area?* (Students might answer this by saying something like, "The cube shape hides some squares inside, so their faces do not get counted in the surface area of the cube. In the long 1-by-1-by-27 arrangement, all the cubes have faces exposed; in the 3-by-3-by-3 arrangement, one cube is completely hidden.")

Have students describe their processes for finding surface area. Students should be at a point at which it is appropriate for you to model a symbolic representation of their strategies. For instance, if a student says something like:

"We found the area of the front, the area of the top, and the area of the right side, then doubled the total."

You could write $(w \times h + w \times \ell + \ell \times h) \times 2$. This is not necessarily to develop a formula that students need to memorize. (Formulas for surface area are complicated, and often more easily reconstructed from a visual or image of the surface area of the prism as the area of the six faces of the prism than memorized.) Instead, it is to encourage the kind of careful thinking required to write a formula.

Check for Understanding

Have students describe the dimensions of the box with the least surface area, and then with the greatest surface area, for 100 cubes.

Then, help the class further explore the minimal surface area.

- *For 12 cubes, you found the arrangement with the least surface area to be a 2-by-2-by-3 box. If you could cut the cubes apart, could you package the same volume with even less surface area?* (The arrangement with the least surface area for 8 and 27 cubes is a cubic box. The 12-cube arrangement raises the issue of whole-number edges versus fractional-length edges for the minimum surface area.)

Students may suggest something like the following: "It's a cube whose dimensions are all the same but when you multiply them together, they equal 12"—in other words, the cube root of the volume. If this comes up, you can use a calculator to guess and check for this number, which is approximately 2.289 or 2.29.

Going Further You may want to ask the class to compare the shapes of animals that live in cold climates to those that live in the desert—for example, a polar bear and a snake. Polar bears are more cube-like in that they are designed with a small surface area compared to their volume. This minimizes the escape of the heat in their warm blood to the cold atmosphere. Snakes have a great deal of surface area compared to their volume, which allows them to quickly use the sunshine to heat their cold blood.

2.2 Saving Trees

Mathematical Goals

- Predict which rectangular prism of those with a common volume will have the smallest surface area
- Refine a strategy for finding the surface area of a rectangular prism

Launch

Review what students discovered in Problem 2.1.

- *How would you describe the shape of the box we found in the last problem that held 24 cubes and had the least amount of surface area?*

Introduce Problem 2.2.

In mathematics, we are always looking for patterns and rules that will help us to predict outcomes. In today's problem, you are challenged to explore prisms with different volumes. You are asked to look carefully at the data and make conjectures about what you think will help you to predict the arrangement with the smallest surface area.

Let the class work on the problem in groups of 3 or 4.

Materials
- Inch cubes
- 2 or 3 rectangular or cubic boxes

Explore

Encourage groups who make conjectures about the arrangement of cubes that requires the least amount of packaging material to test other arrangements of the same number of cubes.

Test your conjectures on a number of cubes other than the 8, 27, and 12 suggested in the problem.

If a group is having trouble with the problem, talk through the case of eight cubes with them. Ask them to build each arrangement and to look at the physical objects as well as the measures in their table.

Look at the dimensions for each arrangement and how they change from one arrangement to another.

- *What is the difference between the box with the greatest surface area and the box with the least surface area?*
- *How does this difference show up in the actual boxes made from cubes?*
- *How does this difference show up in the dimensions of the boxes?*

Summarize

Ask students to explain why the more cube-like rectangular arrangement requires the least packaging material.

Put the boxes with the greatest surface area together and those with the least surface area together.

- *How would you describe these shapes compared to these?*

Materials
- Student notebooks

continued on next page

- *Why is the more cube-like rectangular box the box with the least surface area?*

Have students describe their processes for finding surface area. Model a symbolic representation of their strategies. This is not to develop a formula that students need to memorize. Instead, it is to encourage the kind of careful thinking required to write a formula.

Help the class further explore the minimal surface area.

ACE Assignment Guide for Problem 2.2

Core 4–6
Other *Connections* 23–24; *Extension* 28; unassigned choices from previous problems

Adapted For suggestions about adapting Exercise 5 and other ACE exercises, see the CMP *Special Needs Handbook*.
Connecting to Prior Units 23–24: *Covering and Surrounding*

Answers to Problem 2.2

A. The rectangular arrangements of cubes with the least surface area are:

  1. 8 cubes: 2 by 2 by 2 (surface area: 24 in.^{3})

  2. 27 cubes: 3 by 3 by 3 (surface area: 54 in.^{3})

  3. 12 cubes: 2 by 2 by 3 (surface area: 32 in.^{3})

B. 1. Possible true conjecture: The rectangular arrangement of a given number of cubes with the least surface area is the one that is most like a cube. Students may also use language like *compact* or *shortest* (in contrast to the long, skinny packages). This is similar to the conjecture that students examined in *Covering and Surrounding*: that the rectangle with the smallest perimeter for a given area is a square.

  2. The conjecture in B gives:

  30 cubes: 2 by 3 by 5

  64 cubes: 4 by 4 by 4, each of which has the smallest surface area for the given number of cubes.

  One way to think about justifying the conjecture is that the exposed faces of the small cubes generate the surface area. The more compact (or cube-like) the prism, the more faces of the small cubes face the interior of the prism, so fewer are exposed as surface area.

C. Possible answers: Find the area of each of the six faces and add them together. Find the area of the front, the top, and the right side; add these together and double the answer.

2.3 Filling Rectangular Boxes

Goals

- Understand that prisms can be filled systematically in identical layers, and that this layering leads to the formula for volume

- Develop a formula for finding the volume of a rectangular prism

In this problem, students are helped to think about how to fill the prism systematically. First, they place one layer of cubes on the base. The number of cubes is equal to the area of the base—each cube (or part of a cube) rests on a square (or part of a square) in the base of the prism, so there is a one-to-one correspondence between the number of cubes and the area of the base. Then, they determine how many layers of cubes are needed to fill the box. This is equal to the height of the box. Thus, the volume of the box is the number of cubes in the bottom layer multiplied by the number of layers—the area of the base times the height of the prism.

In a later investigation, students will study cones and spheres. For these shapes, layering is not a useful strategy for thinking about volume. Instead, students will fill these shapes with clay or rice, then pour the contents into a container of known volume.

Launch 2.3

Discuss the Getting Ready. This is an opportunity to help your students think a little bit differently about volume.

Bernie is thinking correctly about volume. There will be a little too much rice for the prism on the right because its volume is 35 cm^3 while the volume of the other prism is 36 cm^3. Students may not know the exact volume, but they may suggest filling one box with rice and pouring it into the other box.

It is helpful at this stage to know whether your students see layers and filling with rice as two ways to measure the same thing. If they do not, you may want to take time to have them fill rectangular prisms with rice and make comparisons of their own.

Talk about Save-a-Tree's ready-made box sizes and ATC Toy Company's decision. Hold up a box.

- *What is the volume of my box? How did you make your estimate?*

Constructing one or all of the boxes from transparent grids might help students visualize the process of finding volume. If you have the time to make the transparent boxes, show them to the class or distribute one box to each pair of students. Ask students to estimate the volume of each box. Record some of the estimates on the board. Tell the class that the intent of this problem is for them to look for efficient ways to find the volume of a box. If some students claim that they already have a rule for finding the volume of a box (volume = $\ell \times w \times h$), question them about it.

Suggested Questions Ask:

- *What does your rule mean?*

- *Why do you think it will work?*

- *Will it work for all prisms?*

Students can work in pairs.

Explore 2.3

Remind students to save the transparent boxes for the summary. Some students may need cubes to simulate filling the boxes.

You may want to suggest that students organize their work in a table. The organization of the following table will help promote the layering strategy for determining volume.

Box	Cubes in a Single Layer	Number of Identical Layers	Volume	Surface Area (optional)
W				
X				
Y				
Z				

As students make progress in their pairs, ask them how close their estimates of the volume were to the answers they are finding.

INVESTIGATION 2

Discuss the answers to Question A. At this point in the unit, two popular strategies for finding the number of blocks that will fill a box are the following:

"First we found a layer for box W. The base is 2 inches by 3 inches, so it takes 6 cubic inches to form one layer. Then we saw that it would take four of these layers to fill the box."

"We used layering, but we saw that for box W, 3 × 2 is the number of blocks in one layer, and 3 × 2 × 4 is the number of blocks in four layers. We think you can just multiply the three dimensions to get the volume of the box."

Suggested Questions If some students offer the formula volume = $\ell \times w \times h$, ask:

- *What does* $\ell \times w \times h$ *mean in terms of counting layers?* [$\ell \times w$ is the area of the base (the number of cubes in the first layer) and *h* is the height (number of layers). The strategy of multiplying the area of the base by the height will work for all prisms and cylinders.]

Talk about the answers to Question B. Students may offer these strategies for finding the surface area of a box:

"We saw that for each box, two faces are the same. So we found the area of each of the three different faces and multiplied each one by 2. Then we just added the three numbers."

"We pictured folding the box Z flat like this:

"We saw that we had one big rectangle (shaded) that is 12 by 10 and two small rectangles that are 2 by 4. So, the surface area is 12 × 10 + 2 × 2 × 4."

The following questions can be used if needed to focus students' attention on the bottom layer of a prism and how many layers it will take to fill the prism.

- *Why is the number of cubes in the bottom layer equal to the area of the base?* (Each square unit of area can be thought of as the base of a unit cube.)

If you have constructed models of the boxes, hold one of them up at the orientation shown in the problem.

- *Make a sketch of this box while I sketch it at the overhead.*

- *What are the dimensions of the base of this box? What is its height? What is the volume of the box?*

- *Now, set the box on a different base.*

- *What is the area of the new base? How many cubes will fit on the base?*

- *How many layers will be needed to fill the box?*

- *Does this new orientation change the volume? Explain your answer.*

- *What is the surface area of this box? Would changing the orientation of the box change its surface area?*

Students should visualize the surface area as the area of the six faces. This provides them with a strategy that will generalize to all prisms. They find the six areas and add them. Some will notice that in rectangular prisms there are three pairs of congruent faces (opposite faces are congruent). This would shorten their calculations slightly. They would find the area of three faces—one from each pair—and multiply by 2.

Give each pair of students a small box and ask them to find its dimensions and volume. Have them check their answers by filling the box with unit cubes. Or you can use the boxes from Problem 1.4 as a quicker assessment.

For Question D, repeat the questions in Questions A and B of Problem 2.3 for Box W, Box X, and Box Y.

2.3 Filling Rectangular Boxes

Mathematical Goals

- Understand that prisms can be filled systematically in identical layers, and that this layering leads to the formula for volume
- Develop a formula for finding the volume of a rectangular prism

Launch

Discuss the Getting Ready.

Talk about Save-a-Tree's ready-made box sizes and ATC Toy Company's decision. Hold up a box.

- *What is the volume of my box? How did you make your estimate?*

Ask students to estimate the volume of each box. Record some of the estimates on the board. Tell the class that the intent of this problem is for them to look for efficient ways to find the volume of a box. If some students claim that they already have a rule for finding the volume of a box (volume = $\ell \times w \times h$), question them about it.

- *What does your rule mean?*
- *Why do you think it will work?*
- *Will it work for all prisms?*

Students can work in pairs.

Materials

- Pre-made box for demonstration
- Transparent grids (optional)
- Transparent models of Boxes W, X, Y, and Z (optional)
- Transparencies 2.3A and 2.3B

Explore

Remind students to save the transparent boxes for the summary. Some students may need cubes to simulate filling the boxes.

You may want to suggest that students organize their work in a table.

As students make progress in their pairs, ask them how close their estimates of the volume were to the answers they are finding.

Materials

- Inch cubes
- Inch or other grid paper

Summarize

Discuss the answers to Question A. If some students offer the formula volume = $\ell \times w \times h$, ask what this means in terms of counting layers. Talk about the answers to Question B. Spend time on students' strategies for finding the surface area of a box.

Ask some questions to probe students' understanding.

- *Why is the number of cubes in the bottom layer equal to the area of the base?*

If you have constructed models of the boxes, hold one of them up at the orientation shown in the problem.

- *What are the dimensions of the base of this box? What is its height? What is the volume of the box?*

Materials

- Student notebooks
- Transparency 2.3C

continued on next page

Now, set the box on a different base.

- *What is the area of the new base? How many cubes will fit on the base? How many layers will be needed to fill the box?*

- *Does this new orientation change the volume? What is the surface area of this box? Would changing the orientation of the box change its surface area?*

Go over the volumes and surface areas of the other boxes.

ACE Assignment Guide for Problem 2.3

Differentiated Instruction
Solutions for All Learners

Core 8–15
Other *Applications* 7, 16–19; *Connections* 25–27; *Extensions* 29; unassigned choices from previous problems

Adapted For suggestions about adapting ACE exercises, see the CMP *Special Needs Handbook*.

Answers to Problem 2.3

A. **1.** 8 cubes

   2. 10 layers

   3. 80 cubes

   4. See the Summarize section for some possible explanations.

B. 136 in.^{2}

C. The volume doesn't change. The number of cubes in the first layer changes, but so does the number of layers. The volume is: area of base × height, or $10 \times 4 \times 2$. In the original position, the volume was $2 \times 4 \times 10$. Similarly, the surface area of the box does not change.

D. Surface area: Box W: 52 in.^{2}; Box X: 54 in.^{2}; Box Y: 132 in.^{2}

   Volume: Box W: 24 cubes; Box X: 27 cubes; Box Y: 80 cubes

Designing Rectangular Boxes

Finding the right box for a product requires thought and planning. A company must consider how much the box can hold as well as the amount and the cost of the material needed to make the box.

The amount that a box can hold depends on its volume. The **volume** of a box is the number of unit cubes that it would take to fill the box. The amount of material needed to make or to cover a box depends on its surface area. The **surface area** of a box is the total area of all of its faces.

The box shown below has dimensions of 1 centimeter by 3 centimeters by 1 centimeter. It would take three 1-centimeter cubes to fill this box, so the box has a volume of 3 cubic centimeters. Because the net for the box takes fourteen 1-centimeter grid squares to make the box, the box has a surface area of 14 square centimeters.

volume = 3 cubic centimeters

surface area = 14 square centimeters

In this investigation, you will explore the possible surface areas for a rectangular box that holds a given volume.

Notes _____

_____

_____

_____

ATC Toy Company is planning to market a set of
children's alphabet blocks. Each block is a cube
with 1-inch edges, so each block has a volume of
1 cubic inch.

Problem 2.1 Finding Surface Area

The company wants to arrange 24 blocks in the shape of a rectangular
prism and then package them in a box that exactly fits the prism.

A. Find all the ways 24 cubes can be arranged into a rectangular prism.
Make a sketch of each arrangement. Record the dimensions and
surface area. It may help to organize your findings into a table like
the one below:

Possible Arrangements of 24 Cubes

Length	Width	Height	Volume	Surface Area	Sketch
■	■	■	■	■	■
■	■	■	■	■	■
■	■	■	■	■	■

B. Which of your arrangements requires the box made with the least
material? Which requires the box made with the most material?

C. Which arrangement would you recommend to ATC Toy Company?
Explain why.

D. Why do you think the company makes 24 alphabet blocks rather
than 26?

ACE Homework starts on page 24.

20 Filling and Wrapping

Notes _____

_____

_____

_____

2.2 Saving Trees

You discovered that 24 blocks can be packaged in different ways that use varying amounts of packaging material. By using less material, a company can save money, reduce waste, and conserve natural resources.

Which rectangular arrangement of cubes uses the least amount of packaging material?

Problem 2.2 Finding the Least Surface Area

A. Explore the possible arrangements of each of the following numbers of cubes. Find the arrangement that requires the least amount of packaging material.

    1. 8 cubes   **2.** 27 cubes   **3.** 12 cubes

B. **1.** Make a conjecture about the rectangular arrangement of cubes that requires the least packaging material.

    2. Does your conjecture work for 30 cubes? Does it work for 64 cubes? If not, change your conjecture so it works for any number of cubes. When you have a conjecture that you think is correct, give reasons why you think your conjecture is valid.

C. Describe a strategy for finding the total surface area of a closed box.

ACE Homework starts on page 24.

Notes _____

_____

_____

_____

Did You Know?

Area is expressed in square units, such as square inches or square centimeters. You can abbreviate square units by writing the abbreviation for the unit followed by a raised 2. For example, an abbreviation for square inches is in.^{2}.

Volume is expressed in cubic units. You can abbreviate cubic units by writing the abbreviation for the unit followed by a raised 3. For example, an abbreviation for cubic centimeters is cm^3.

Getting Ready for Problem 2.3

One seventh-grade student, Bernie, wonders if he can compare volumes without having to calculate them exactly. He figures that volume measures the contents of a container. He fills the prism on the left with rice and then pours the rice into the one on the right.

- How can you decide if there is enough rice or too much rice to fill the prism on the right?

2.3 Filling Rectangular Boxes

A company may have boxes custom-made to package its products. However, a company may also buy ready-made boxes. The Save-a-Tree packaging company sells ready-made boxes in several sizes.

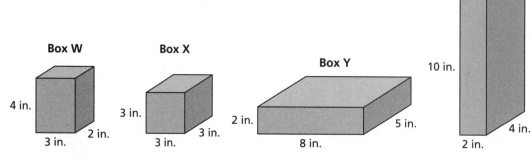

22 Filling and Wrapping

STUDENT PAGE

Notes _____

_____

_____

_____

(22) 50

ATC Toy Company is considering using Save-a-Tree's Box Z to ship alphabet blocks. Each block is a 1-inch cube. ATC needs to know how many blocks will fit into Box Z and the surface area of the box.

A. The number of unit cubes that fit in a box is the volume of the box.

10 in.

4 in.

2 in.

1. How many cubes will fit in a single layer at the bottom of this box?

2. How many identical layers can be stacked in this box?

3. What is the total number of cubes that can be packed in this box?

4. Consider the number of cubes in each layer, the number of layers, the volume, and the dimensions of the box. What connections do you see among these measurements?

B. Find the surface area of Box Z.

C. Suppose Box Z is put down on its side so its base is 4 inches by 10 inches and its height is 2 inches. Does this affect the volume of the box? Does this affect the surface area? Explain your reasoning.

2 in.

4 in.

10 in.

D. Apply your strategies for finding volume and surface area to Boxes W, X, and Y.

ACE Homework starts on page 24.

Investigation 2 Designing Rectangular Boxes **23**

Notes _____

_____

_____

_____

Applications

In Exercises 1–3, rectangular prisms are made using 1-inch cubes.

    a. Find the length, width, and height of each prism.

    b. Find the amount of material needed to make a box for each prism.

    c. Find the number of cubes in each prism.

1.

2.

3.

4. Suppose you plan to make a box that will hold exactly 40 one-inch cubes.

    a. Give the dimensions of all the possible boxes you can make.

    b. Which box has the least surface area? Which box has the greatest surface area?

    c. Why might you want to know the dimensions of the box with the least surface area?

5. Each of these boxes holds 36 ping-pong balls.

48 cm

16 cm
12 cm
12 cm

8 cm
24 cm
12 cm

24 cm
8 cm
12 cm

12 cm
4 cm

    a. Without figuring, which box has the least surface area? Why?

    b. Check your guess by finding the surface area of each box.

24   Filling and Wrapping

Notes _____

_____

_____

_____

6. a. The box at the right is a $6 \times 2 \times 1$ arrangement of drink cans. Suppose the dimensions of the box are, in centimeters, $39 \times 13 \times 12.25$. Compare the surface area of the box with the more traditional $4 \times 3 \times 1$ arrangement, which measures, in centimeters, $26 \times 19.5 \times 12.25$.

b. The box at the right is a $4 \times 3 \times 2$ arrangement of drink cans. Suppose the dimensions of the box are, in centimeters, $26 \times 19.5 \times 24.5$. Compare the surface area of the box with the more traditional $6 \times 4 \times 1$ arrangement, which measures, in centimeters, $39 \times 26 \times 12.25$.

7. a. Sketch a rectangular box with dimensions 2 centimeters by 7 centimeters by 3 centimeters.

b. What is the surface area of the box?

c. Draw a net for the box on grid paper. What is the relationship between the area of the net and the surface area of the box?

In Exercises 8–10, rectangular prisms are drawn using inch cubes.

a. Find the length, width, and height of each prism.

b. Find the volume of each prism. Describe how you found the volume.

c. Find the surface area of each prism. Describe how you found the surface area.

8.

9.

10.

Notes _____

_____

_____

_____

11. a. What is the total number of cubes, including the cubes already shown, needed to fill the closed box below?

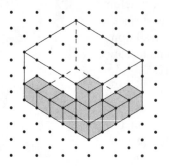

b. What is the surface area of the box?

For Exercises 12–14, find the volume and surface area of the closed box.

12.

4 in.
2 in.
4 in.

13.

10 in.
4.5 in.
1.5 in.

14.

2.5 in.
6 in.
6.8 in.

15. a. Make a sketch of a closed box with dimensions 2 centimeters by 3 centimeters by 5 centimeters.

b. How many centimeter cubes will fit in one layer at the bottom of the box?

c. How many layers are needed to fill the box?

d. Find the volume of the box.

e. Find the surface area of the box.

16. Mr. Turner's classroom is 20 feet wide, 30 feet long, and 10 feet high.

a. Sketch a scale model of the classroom. Label the dimensions of the classroom on your sketch.

Notes _____

_____

_____

_____

b. Find the volume of the classroom. Why might this information be useful?

c. Find the total area of the walls, the floor, and the ceiling. Why might this information be useful?

17. Each expression below will help you to find the volume or surface area of one of the boxes pictured. Simplify each expression. Decide whether you have found a volume or a surface area, and for which box.

Homework Help Online PHSchool.com
For: Help with Exercise 17
Web Code: ane-6217

a. $2 \times (3.5 \times 5.7) + 2 \times (5.7 \times 12) + 2 \times (3.5 \times 12)$

b. $6\frac{1}{4} \times 6$ **c.** $6 \times 6\frac{1}{2}$ **d.** $2\frac{1}{3} \times 2\frac{2}{5} \times 5$

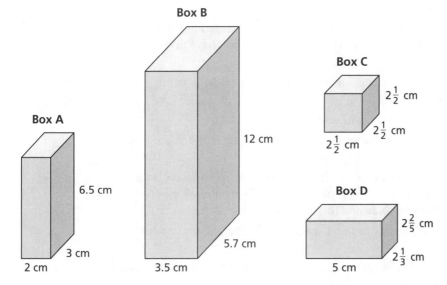

Box B

12 cm

5.7 cm

3.5 cm

Box A

6.5 cm

3 cm

2 cm

Box C

$2\frac{1}{2}$ cm

$2\frac{1}{2}$ cm

$2\frac{1}{2}$ cm

Box D

$2\frac{2}{5}$ cm

$2\frac{1}{3}$ cm

5 cm

Investigation 2 Designing Rectangular Boxes   **27**

Notes _____

_____

_____

_____

18. The city of Centerville plans to dig a rectangular landfill. The landfill will have a base with dimensions 700 ft by 200 ft and a depth of 85 ft.

a. How many cubic feet of garbage will the landfill hold?

b. What information do you need to determine how long the landfill can be used until it is full?

c. Centerville hires an excavator to dig the hole for the landfill. How many cubic yards of dirt will he have to haul away?

19. Describe the dimensions of a rectangular prism with a volume of 80 cubic inches but a surface area of less than 132 square inches.

Connections

20. a. There is only one way to arrange five identical cubes into the shape of a rectangular prism. Sketch the rectangular prism made from five identical cubes.

b. Find more numbers of cubes that can be arranged into a rectangular prism in only one way. What do these numbers have in common?

21. a. Sketch every rectangular prism that can be made from ten identical cubes.

b. Find the surface area of each prism you sketched.

c. Give the dimensions of the prism that has the least surface area.

22. a. Each of the boxes you designed in Problem 2.1 had a rectangular base and a height. Use a graph to show the relationship between the area of the base and the height of each box.

b. Describe the relationship between the height and the area of the base.

c. How might your graph be useful to a packaging engineer at ATC Toy Company?

Notes _____

_____

_____

_____

23. The dimensions of the recreation center floor are 150 ft by 45 ft, and the walls are 10 ft high. A gallon of paint will cover 400 ft². About how much paint is needed to paint the walls of the recreation center?

24. If a small can of paint will cover 1,400 square inches, about how many small cans are needed to paint the walls of the recreation center described in Exercise 23?

For Exercises 25–27, use the three given views of a three-dimensional building to sketch the building. Then, find its volume.

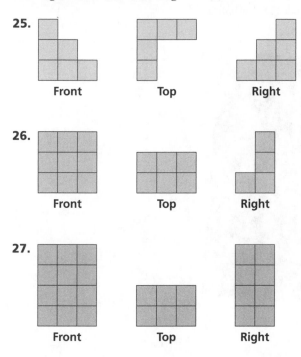

25.

Front   Top   Right

26.

Front   Top   Right

27.

Front   Top   Right

Notes _____

_____

_____

_____

Extensions

28. Many drinks are packaged in rectangular boxes of 24 cans.

    a. During the spring of 1993, a company announced that it was going to package 24 twelve-ounce cans into a more cube-like shape. Why might the company have decided to change their packaging?

    b. List all the ways 24 twelve-ounce cans of soda can be arranged and packaged in a rectangular box. Which arrangement do you recommend that a drink company use? Why?

29. Slam Dunk Sporting Goods packages its basketballs in cubic boxes with 1-foot edges. For shipping, the company packs 12 basketballs (in its boxes) into a large rectangular shipping box.

    a. Find the dimensions of every possible shipping box into which the boxes of basketballs would exactly fit.

    b. Find the surface area of each shipping box in part (a).

    c. Slam Dunk uses the shipping box that requires the least material. Which shipping box does it use?

    d. Slam Dunk decides to ship basketballs in boxes of 24. It wants to use the shipping box that requires the least material. Find the dimensions of the box it should use. How much more packaging material is needed to ship 24 basketballs than to ship 12 basketballs?

Notes _____

_____

_____

_____

Mathematical Reflections 2

In this investigation, you arranged cubes in the shape of rectangular prisms, and you also found the arrangements with the least and greatest surface area. You developed methods for finding surface area and volume. These questions will help you summarize what you have learned.

Think about your answers to these questions. Discuss your ideas with other students and your teacher. Then write a summary of your findings in your notebook.

1. For a given number of cubes, what arrangement will give a rectangular prism with the least surface area? What arrangement will give a rectangular prism with the greatest surface area? Use specific examples to illustrate your ideas.

2. Describe how you can find the surface area of a rectangular prism. Give a rule for finding the surface area.

3. Describe how you can find the volume of any prism. Give a rule for finding the volume.

Notes _____

_____

_____

_____

Investigation 2

ACE
Assignment Choices

Differentiated Instruction
Solutions for All Learners

Problem 2.1
Core 1–3, 20
Other *Connections* 21, 22

Problem 2.2
Core 4–6
Other *Connections* 23–24, *Extensions* 28; unassigned choices from previous problems

Problem 2.3
Core 8–15
Other *Applications* 7, 16–19; *Connections* 25–27; *Extensions* 29; unassigned choices from previous problems

Adapted For suggestions about adapting Exercise 5 and other ACE exercises, see the CMP *Special Needs Handbook*.
Connecting to Prior Units 20: *Prime Time*; 22: *Variables and Patterns*; 23, 24: *Covering and Surrounding*

Applications

(Note: To find the number of blocks in Exercises 1–3, some students may count cubes; others may multiply measures. To find the surface area, some students may try to count the faces of the cubes shown; some may add the areas of the faces. What is important at this stage is that they understand that the amount of wrapping is called the *surface area*.)

1. a. $\ell = 5$ in., $w = 3$ in., $h = 1$ in.
  b. 46 in.^{2}
  c. 15 cubes

2. a. $\ell = 5$ in., $w = 3$ in., $h = 2$ in.
  b. 62 in.^{2}
  c. 30 cubes

3. a. $\ell = 5$ in., $w = 3$ in., $h = 5$ in.
  b. 110 in.^{2}
  c. 75 cubes

4. a. There are six possible boxes: 1 by 1 by 40, 1 by 2 by 20, 1 by 4 by 10, 1 by 5 by 8, 2 by 2 by 10, and 2 by 4 by 5.
  b. The 2-by-4-by-5 box has the least surface area, 76 in.^{2}. The 1-by-1-by-40 box has the greatest surface area, 162 in.^{2}.
  c. Possible answer: It will cost less to make the box with the least surface area. Also, it might be easier to pack these boxes into a larger box.

5. a. Box A, being closest to a cube, has the least surface area.
  b. Box A: 1,056 cm^2
  Boxes B and C: 1,152 cm^2
  Box D: 1,632 cm^2

6. a. The arrangement closest to the cube, the $4 \times 3 \times 1$ pack, has the lesser surface area (2,128.75 cm^2 versus 2,288 cm^2 for the $6 \times 2 \times 1$ pack) and requires the lesser amount of material to produce.
  b. The arrangement closest to a cube, the $4 \times 3 \times 2$ pack, has the lesser surface area (3,243.5 cm^2 versus 3,620.5 cm^2 for the $6 \times 4 \times 1$ pack) and requires the lesser amount of material to produce.

7. a. Possible sketch:

7 cm
3 cm   2 cm

  b. 82 cm^2

c. Possible net:

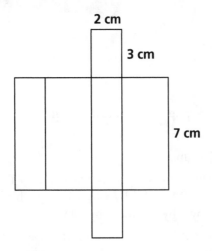

2 cm

3 cm

7 cm

The area of the net is the same as the surface area of the prism.

8. a. $\ell = 5$ in., $w = 4$ in., $h = 1$ in.

  b. 20 in.^{3}

  c. 58 in.^{2}

9. a. $\ell = 5$ in., $w = 4$ in., $h = 5$ in.

  b. 100 in.^{3}

  c. 130 in.^{2}

10. a. $\ell = 5$ in., $w = 4$ in., $h = 2$ in.

  b. 40 in.^{3}

  c. 76 in.^{2}

11.a. 60 cubes are needed to fill the box.

  b. 94 square units

12. Volume is 32 in.^{3}

Surface area is 64 in.^{2}

13. Volume is 67.5 in.^{3}

Surface area is 133.5 in.^{2}

14. Volume is 102 in.^{3}

Surface area is 145.6 in.^{2}

15. a. Possible sketch:

5 cm

3 cm   2 cm

b. In the sketch of part (a), 6 cm cubes would fit in one layer. Students who drew their boxes in different orientations may have either 15 or 10 cm cubes in one layer.

c. In the sketch above, 5 layers would fill the box. Depending on the sketch, 2 or 3 layers are also possible.

d. 30 cm^3

e. 62 cm^2

16. a. Possible sketch:

10 ft

30 ft

20 ft

b. The volume of the room is 6,000 ft^3. This information would be useful for determining the amount of heating and air conditioning the room requires.

c. The total area of the walls, floor, and ceiling (including windows and doors) is 2,200 ft^2. This information would be useful for determining the amount of paint, carpeting, and ceiling tiles the room requires.

17. a. 260.7. This is the surface area, in square centimeters, of Box B.

b. $37\frac{1}{2}$. This is the surface area, in square centimeters, of Box C. (The 6 corresponds to the number of faces on the cube; the $6\frac{1}{4}$ corresponds to the area of each face.)

c. 39. This is the volume, in cubic centimeters, of Box A. (The 6 corresponds to the area of the base, the $6\frac{1}{2}$ corresponds to the height of the prism.)

d. 28. This is the volume, in cubic centimeters, of Box D.

18. a. 11,900,000 ft^3

b. You need to know the size of the population and how much garbage, on average, each person produces in a given period of time. More directly, you need to know the total volume of garbage the city produces in a given period of time.

c. Because there are $3 \times 3 \times 3 = 27$ ft^3 in one cubic yard, there are $11,900,000 \div 27 \approx 440,741$ yd^3 of dirt.

19. A box with whole number dimensions 4 in. by 4 in. by 5 in. This would have the same volume as boxes Y and Z, but would have a smaller surface area of 112 in.^{2}.

(**Note:** Students might choose dimensions which are not whole numbers.)

Connections

20. a. Possible sketch (other sketches may be oriented differently):

b. Other numbers of cubes that can be arranged in only one way to make a rectangular prism are 7, 11, and 13. These are all prime numbers.

21. a. Possible sketches.

b. The 1-by-1-by-10 prism has a surface area of 42 square units; the 1-by-2-by-5 prism has a surface area of 34 square units.

c. 1-by-2-by-5 has the least surface area

22. a.

Area of Base (sq. in.)	Height (in.)
1	24
2	12
3	8
4	6
6	4
8	3
12	2
24	1

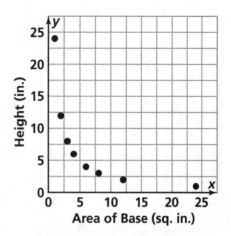

b. As the area of the base increases, the height must decrease.

c. The graph might be helpful in estimating the height of a package with a given base.

23. The total area to be painted is
$2(150 \times 10) + 2(45 \times 10) = 3,900$ ft^2.
$3,900 \div 400 = 9.75$. Thus, about 10 gallons of paint are needed.

24. There are 144 in.^{2} in 1 ft^2, so the total area to be painted is $3,900 \times 144 = 561,600$ in.^{2}. A small can of paint covers 1,400 in.^{2}, so the job will require $561,600 \div 1,400 \approx 401.1$, or about 402 cans.

25. Sketches will vary. Possible sketch:

Volume: Between 7 and 9 cubic units.
Note: There might be some hidden blocks.

26. Sketches will vary. Possible sketch:

Volume: Between 10 and 12 cubic units
Note: There might be some hidden blocks.

27. Sketches will vary. Possible sketch:

Volume: Between 18 and 24 cubic units.
Note: There might be some hidden blocks.

Extensions

28. a. A cube-like shape requires less packaging material. The company may have been responding to environmental concerns of consumers. They may also have wanted to change their packaging to get consumers' attention.

b. The possible arrangements are 1 by 1 by 24, 1 by 2 by 12, 1 by 3 by 8, 1 by 4 by 6, 2 by 2 by 6, and 2 by 3 by 4. Because the height of a drink can is not the same as its diameter, different permutations of these dimensions may be considered. (For instance, a height of 24 cans is different from a length of 24 cans.)

Possible recommendation: The 1-by-1-by-24 looks like more product, but would be quite difficult to carry; the 2-by-2-by-6 may be the easiest to carry, and the 2-by-3-by-4 may save packaging materials.

29. a. 1 by 1 by 12, 1 by 2 by 6, 1 by 3 by 4, and 2 by 2 by 3

b. The surface areas of the boxes above are 50 ft^2, 40 ft^2, 38 ft^2, and 32 ft^2.

c. The 2-by-2-by-3 box .

d. Any of the previous arrangements shown, with one of its dimensions doubled, will result in a box that would hold 24 basketballs. The one that uses the least amount of material is a 2-by-3-by-4 box, requiring 52 ft^2 of material, 20 ft^2 more than the box that requires the least amount of material to hold 12 basketballs.

Possible Answers to Mathematical Reflections

1. The cube arrangements that give prisms with the greatest surface area are those that are long and thin, and those that have the least surface area are those that are most like cubes. For example, for 36 cubes, a 1-by-1-by-36 arrangement has 146 square units of surface area (the greatest possible); a 3-by-3-by-4 arrangement has 66 square units of surface area (the least possible).

For the Teacher If the sides of a rectangular prism are real numbers, then, for a prism with a volume of 36 cubic units, a cube with side lengths $\sqrt[3]{36}$ would have the least surface area.

2. The surface area of a rectangular prism is the total number of square units of area on all of its faces. This can be found by adding together the area of each face or by adding the area of three different faces and doubling it (because opposite faces have equal area).

Note: Because opposite faces of a box have equal area, this is really saying that:

Surface area $= 2(\ell \times w) + 2(w \times h) + 2(\ell \times h)$ or

Surface area $= 2 \times (\ell \times w + w \times h + \ell \times h)$

However, it is not worth the time to memorize this formula. It is just as quick and easy to find the area of the faces and add them together.

3. The volume of a rectangular prism can be found by taking the number of unit cubes that would fit in the base (which is the area of the base) and multiplying that by the number of layers of unit cubes it would take to completely fill the prism. This number of layers represents the height of the prism. Thus,

Volume = area of the base of the prism × height of the prism.

Because it is a rectangular prism, the area of the base is $\ell \times w$. Thus, volume $= \ell \times w \times h$, where ℓ and w represent the length and width of the rectangular base, and h represents the height of the prism.

Investigation 3 — Prisms and Cylinders

Mathematical and Problem-Solving Goals

- Develop understanding of volume and surface area of prisms
- Develop a strategy for finding the volume of a cylinder using its dimensions
- Connect this strategy to the idea of layers in rectangular and other prisms
- Develop a strategy for finding the surface area of a cylinder
- Apply understanding of volume to solve problems
- Understand that a variety of different three-dimensional figures can have the same volume but different surface areas

Summary of Problems

Problem 3.1 Filling Fancy Boxes

Students compare the volumes and surface areas of a variety of rectangular prisms with regular bases and a common height.

Problem 3.2 Filling Cylinders

Students extend their thinking about layers in rectangular prisms to develop a strategy for finding the volume of a cylinder.

Problem 3.3 Making Cylinders and Prisms From Nets

Students consider nets for prisms and cylinders to determine the surface areas of these solids.

Problem 3.4 Making a New Juice Container

Students design a rectangular box with the same volume as a given cylinder.

	Suggested Pacing	Materials for Students	Materials for Teachers	ACE Assignments
All	5 days	Calculators, colored pens, pencils or markers, blank transparencies and transparency markers (optional)	Blank transparencies and transparency markers	
3.1	$1\frac{1}{2}$ days	Scissors, blank paper, tape, inch cubes, inch grid paper	Transparency 3.1; sample prisms and unit cubes; 8.5 in. by 11 in. sheets of paper; macaroni or rice	1, 23–25
3.2	1 day	Cylinders, Labsheet 3.2 (two per student), scissors, paper, tape, inch cubes, inch grid paper	Transparencies 3.2A and 3.2B; sheets of paper; cm cubes	2–14, 26–30
3.3	1 day	Labsheets 3.3A and 3.3B (one of each per student), scissors, cm grid paper, tape	Transparencies 3.3A and 3.3B	15–17, 31, 32
3.4	1 day	Colored pencils or markers, scissors, cm grid paper, transparent tape	Cylindrical and/or rectangular juice containers (optional)	18–22, 33–35
MR	$\frac{1}{2}$ day			

Useful Models to Introduce the Unit

To introduce this investigation, it might be helpful to show a variety of different prisms and cylinders. Cans and juice-concentrate containers make good models of cylinders. One or two of your sample cylinders should be transparent; look for candy or nut boxes made from clear plastic, borrow some transparent cylindrical beakers from the science teacher, or make some containers from transparency film. Cardboard rolls from paper towels and wrapping paper are easy to cut apart to demonstrate that the lateral surface of a cylinder is a rectangle. Fancy chocolate is sometimes packaged in a box shaped like a triangular prism.

You may also want to obtain (perhaps borrow) a set of manufactured solids. The clear plastic models are particularly useful, because they allow students to work with volume concepts. A cone, sphere, cylinder, cube, and rectangular prism would be particularly helpful.

Filling Fancy Boxes

Goal

• Develop understanding of volume and surface area of prisms

In this problem, students discover that their strategy for finding the volume of a rectangular prism applies to any right rectangular prism.

Launch 3.1

If possible, have a few non-rectangular prisms to show the class.

Demonstrate how to make a prism from a sheet of paper. (Grid paper works well.) Be sure to stress the importance of marking and folding the paper so that the shortest dimension is the height of each prism.

• *In this problem, you will construct four types of prisms and a cylinder from paper. You will have to imagine that these prisms have tops and bottoms. You will compare their volumes and surface areas.*

• *Make a conjecture about the volumes of the prisms and cylinders. Are they the same?*

Collect some answers. Some students may suggest using a layering method similar to the strategy used to find the volume of rectangular prisms. Because the problem asks students to compare, some students may suggest filling the containers with unit cubes or sand or beans.

• *Make a conjecture about the surface area of each prism. Are the surface areas the same?*

Collect some answers. Because identical pieces of paper are used for each prism, students may initially believe that they all have the same surface area. This is acceptable as a conjecture at this point. Be alert while students are exploring to make sure they realize that the surface area will also include the areas of the ends of each prism.

Have unit cubes and other material that students can use to fill the containers available. You can use popped popcorn, small macaroni, beans, or rice.

Let students work in groups of 3 or 4 to construct the prisms. (If time is an issue, you can do this investigation as a demonstration.)

Explore 3.1

Give each group several sheets of plain paper (for constructing the paper prisms; scrap paper would be fine), a few sheets of inch (or cm) grid paper on which to place the prisms, transparent tape, and one-inch cubes or centimeter cubes.

If students need help folding the pentagonal prism, suggest that they mark off five equal segments on the top and bottom edges of the paper and use the marks to make the folds. (Some will remember the strategies they used to fold fraction strips in the grade 6 units *Bits and Pieces I* and *Bits and Pieces II*.)

Allow the groups to compare the volumes using any method they want. Some may try the layering method that was used for rectangular prisms and some may use unit cubes, popcorn, and so on to fill the boxes and note that as the number of sides of the prism increases, the volume increases.

If students are using the layer method, they may find the number of cubes in the first layer either by estimating the area of the base or placing cubes on the base and estimating the number of partial cubes needed to complete it.

Some may want to be exact and will remember finding area in the grade 6 unit *Covering and Surrounding*. Students should know how to find the area of triangles, rectangles, parallelograms, and circles, and how to divide other figures into these basic figures whose areas they can calculate.

Summarize 3.1

Call on different groups to demonstrate and share their strategies for comparing volumes. If you have transparent containers, students can use these in the summary. If they are filling the containers with cubes or something else, the difference in volumes will be noticeable. You may want to construct a few more paper or transparent prisms to extend this discussion.

Here are some ways students may compare volumes:

• Fill the triangular prism with rice. Then pour this amount into the square prism. Mark the height of the rice. Continue with the next two prisms—pour in the rice from the triangular prism and mark the height. As the number of sides of the base of a prism increases, the volume increases.

- Start with the hexagonal prism. Fill the prism with large beans or some similar material. Then pour these beans into the next smaller prism and collect the overflow of beans that do not fit into the prism. Estimate the overflow. Continue with a couple of the other prisms.

- Some students may use a layering strategy to find the volume of prisms. In this case, they will compute or estimate the volume in unit cubes. See the discussion at the end of Problem 3.3.

Ask students about the results of their comparisons.

- *How does the shape change as the number of sides of the base polygon increases?* (The shape looks more and more like a cylinder. Of these shapes, the prism with the greatest number of sides of the base polygon has the greatest volume.)

Hold up some other prisms (e.g. with an octagonal base) made the same way if you have them or ask students to imagine a prism with more edges in the base, but the same height.

- *Compare the volume of this prism with the ones in the problem.*

Discuss students' suggestions for finding surface area.

- *Compare your methods for finding the surface area of a rectangular prism to any prism.* (They are the same: find the area of the sides and bases and add them together.)

Students will note that lateral surface areas are the same for the prisms and cylinders, but that the areas of the bases are different. They may be able to see that the area of the base is increasing as the number of sides increases. This is why the volume increases as well.

Surface area will be discussed in more detail in Problem 3.3.

If you have models of the prisms made from transparency film, you can use them to demonstrate the generality of the 'layering method' to find volume. This might be helpful for students who may still be struggling with the layering idea. You can fill in layers with unit cubes one layer at a time or with rice one centimeter deep at a time.

Hold up a prism that is not rectangular.

- *What do you think the volume of this prism is?*

- *How might you find its volume?*

- *How many cubes will fit in the first layer? How would you find out?*

- *How many layers will there be? How would you find out?*

3.1 Filling Fancy Boxes

Mathematical Goal

- Develop understanding of volume and surface area of prisms

Launch

If possible, have a few non-rectangular prisms to show the class.

Demonstrate how to make a prism from a sheet of paper. Stress the importance of folding the paper so that the shortest dimension is the height of each prism.

- *Make a conjecture about the volumes of the prisms and cylinders. Are they the same?*

Collect some answers.

- *Make a conjecture about the surface area of each prism. Are the surface areas the same?*

Collect some answers. Have unit cubes and other material that students can use to fill the containers available. You can use popped popcorn, small macaroni, beans, or rice.

Let students work in groups of 3 or 4 to construct the prisms.

Materials
- Scissors
- Blank paper
- Tape
- Transparency 3.1
- Sample prisms
- Inch grid paper
- Inch cubes
- Macaroni, beans, or rice for filling containers (optional)

Vocabulary
- cylinder
- prism

Explore

Allow the groups to compare the volumes using any method they want.

Some may want to be exact and will remember finding area in the grade 6 unit *Covering and Surrounding*. Students should know how to find the area of triangles, rectangles, parallelograms, and circles and how to divide other figures into these basic figures whose area they can calculate.

Summarize

Call on different groups to demonstrate and share their strategies for comparing volumes.

Ask students about the results of their comparisons.

- *How does the shape change as the number of sides of the base polygon increases?*

Hold up some other prisms (e.g., with an octagonal base) made the same way if you have them:

- *Compare the volume of this prism with the ones in the problem.*

Discuss students' suggestions for finding surface area.

- *Compare your methods for finding the surface area of a rectangular prism to any prism.*

Surface area will be discussed in more detail in Problem 3.3.

Materials
- Student notebooks

ACE Assignment Guide for Problem 3.1

Core 1

Other *Connections* 23–25

Adapted For suggestions about adapting ACE exercises, see the CMP *Special Needs Handbook*.
Connecting to Prior Units 23: *Covering and Surrounding*; 24: *Comparing and Scaling*

Answers to Problem 3.1

A. Each group should have a set of four prisms whose heights are 8.5 in.

B. It may be apparent to some students that the bases of these prisms will have different areas, so the prisms will have different volumes. Other students may well believe that the areas will be the same because they are aware that the perimeters of the bases are the same. They are not the same. Carefully folded and measured prisms will have larger volumes for a larger number of sides. Some students may try to calculate the volume by finding the number of unit cubes in a layer and then multiplying this number by the height (number of layers). Perfectly folded and measured prisms made from $8\frac{1}{2}$ in. by 11 in. pieces of paper will have the following volumes:

> 3 sides: 49.48 in.^{3}
>
> 4 sides: 64.28 in.^{3}
>
> 5 sides: 70.78 in.^{3}
>
> 6 sides: 74.22 in.^{3}

See the discussion at the end of Problem 3.3 for a more detailed discussion on finding the volume of any prism.

C. Students might suggest that the surface area is the area of the 8.5 in. by 11 in. sheet of paper plus the area of the top and base or twice the area of the base (because the top and bottom are congruent shapes).

Note: These prisms have different volumes and surface areas because the bases have different areas.

Some students might be ready to compute the surface area. Each prism would have a lateral surface of 93.5 in.^{2} (the area of the paper) plus twice the area of the base. Therefore, the prism with the largest base (in terms of area) will have the largest surface area. The areas of the bases are:

> 3 sides: $\approx$ 5.83 in.^{2}
>
> 4 sides: $\approx$ 7.56 in.^{2}
>
> 5 sides: $\approx$ 8.33 in.^{2}
>
> 6 sides: $\approx$ 8.73 in.^{2}

D. As the number of faces of a prism with a regular base and constant height increases, the surface area and volume both increase.

Filling Cylinders

Goals

- Develop a strategy for finding the volume of a cylinder using its dimensions

- Connect this strategy to the idea of layers in rectangular and other prisms

- Begin to develop a strategy for finding the surface area of a cylinder

In this problem, students make cylinders from rectangular sheets of paper. They compare two cylinders made in a different way, but from the same piece of paper. Use 8.5 in.-by-11 in. paper. These will have dimensions and bases to match the bases on Labsheet 3.2.

Launch 3.2

Suggested Questions Ask:

- *How does the shape of a prism change as the number of sides of the base increases?* (It becomes more cylindrical in shape.)

Roll a sheet of paper to make a cylinder whose height is the shorter edge of the paper. Ask:

- *How does the volume of a prism change as the number of sides of the base increases?* (It increases.)

- *What do you think will be the relationship among the prisms and this cylinder with the same height?* (Some will conjecture that the volume is greater.)

- *We don't want to always have to pour and measure or fill and count to find the volume of a container. Is there a way to find the volume of a cylinder without filling it with cubes or something else?*

If students don't bring up what they learned in their work with rectangular prisms, drop a few centimeter cubes in the cylinder.

- *If I fill this container with centimeter cubes, will that help me find its volume?* (Yes, it would give an estimate of the volume but wouldn't be very accurate.)

Now roll an identical sheet of paper to make the longer side be the height.

- *How does the volume of this cylinder compare to the first one that I made?*

After the class has made some conjectures about the volumes, distribute Labsheet 3.2 and the sheets of paper.

Let the class work in groups of 2–3.

Explore 3.2

This is an opportunity to see if students remember how to find the area of a circle. If some were not in CMP in 6th grade or forgot the formula, ask other members in the group to explain how to find the area of a circle based on the *radius squares*.

Summarize 3.2

You could use popcorn or something similar to compare the volumes of the two cylinders in Question A.

Describe the method you used to find the volume. Some may find the area using the formula for finding the area of a circle. Some students may just count the squares that cover the base of the cylinders to find the area and the number of blocks in the bottom layer. Push further:

- *If you know the area of the base and the height of the cylinder, how can you find its volume?* (The area of the base times the height of the cylinder.)

- *Explain why this works.* (The area of base tells you how many unit cubes fit in the bottom layer of cubes and the height tells you how many layers of cubes will exactly fill the cylinder.)

- *Compare this method with the one you used to find the volume of prisms.* (They are the same. You find how many unit cubes will fit in one layer of the cylinder and then you find how many layers it takes to fill the cylinder.)

All students should be able to make this connection: the area of the base of the cylinder multiplied by the cylinder's height gives the volume of the cylinder. The next step may be challenging for a number of students: Seeing that if we know the radius of the cylinder, we can find the area of the base and therefore, we can find the cylinder's volume. Spend some time on this idea now and return to it in the next problem.

- *If you know the height and radius of the base of a cylinder, how can you find its volume? Explain why this works.* (Use the radius to find the area of the base and then proceed as in the answer to the previous question.)

Question D can be used to assess students' understanding of volume of a cylinder. Then move to comparing the surface areas of the two model cylinders.

- *Compare the surface areas of the two cylinders.* (They both have the same lateral surface area, but the base of the one with the shortest height is greater than the other base, so its surface area is greater.)

- *Describe a way to find the surface area of the cylinders.*

A rule for finding surface area of a cylinder continues in the next problem.

3.2 Filling Cylinders

Mathematical Goals

- Develop a strategy for finding the volume of a cylinder using its dimensions
- Connect this strategy to the idea of layers in rectangular and other prisms
- Begin to develop a strategy for finding the surface area of a cylinder

Launch

- *How does the shape of a prism change as the number of sides of the base increases?*

Roll a sheet of paper to make a cylinder whose height is the shorter side. Ask:

- *How does the volume of a prism change as the number of sides of the base increases? We don't want to always have to pour and measure or fill and count to find the volume of a container. Is there a way to find the volume of a cylinder without filling it with cubes or something else?*

If students don't bring up what they learned in their work with rectangular prisms, drop a few centimeter cubes in the cylinder.

- *If I fill this container with centimeter cubes, will that help me find its volume?*

Now roll the sheet of paper to have the height be 11 in.

- *How does the volume of this cylinder compare to the first one that I made?*

After the class has made some conjectures about the volumes, pass out Labsheet 3.2. Let the class work in groups of 2–3.

Materials

- Cylinder
- Scissors
- Tape
- Paper
- Cm cubes
- Cm grid paper
- Transparencies 3.2A and 3.2B
- Labsheet 3.2
- Inch cubes and inch grid paper (students)

Explore

This is an opportunity to see if students remember how to find the area of a circle. If some were not in CMP in sixth grade or forgot the formula, ask other members in the group to explain how to find the area of a circle based on the *radius squares*.

Summarize

You could use popcorn or something similar to compare the volumes of the two cylinders in Question A.

- *Describe the method you used to find the volume.*

Push further:

- *If you know the area of the base and the height of the cylinder, how can you find its volume? Explain why this works. Compare this method with the one you used to find the volume of prisms.*

Materials

- Student notebooks
- Popcorn, sand, macaroni, or rice (optional)

continued on next page

Spend some time now on the idea that if we know the radius of the cylinder, we can find the area of the base and, thus, the volume of the cylinder.

Question D can be used to assess students' understanding of the volume of a cylinder. Then move to comparing the surface areas of the cylinders.

- *Describe a way to find the surface area of cylinders.*

A rule for finding the surface area of a cylinder continues in the next problem.

ACE Assignment Guide for Problem 3.2

Core 2, 8–12, 26
Other *Applications* 3–7, 13–14; *Connections* 27–30; unassigned choices from previous problems

Adapted For suggestions about adapting ACE exercises, see the CMP *Special Needs Handbook*.
Connecting to Prior Units 27: *Variables and Patterns*; 29, 30: *Bits and Pieces II*

Answers to Problem 3.2

A. Each group should have two cylinders—one whose height is 11 in. and circumference is 8.5 in. and one whose height is 8.5 in. and circumference is 11 in.

B. The answers will vary.

C. 1. About 5.7 cubes would be in the bottom layer of the taller cylinder. About 9.6 cubes would fit in the bottom layer of the shorter cylinder.

2. 11 layers in the taller cylinder; 8.5 layers in the shorter cylinder.

3. The volume of the taller cylinder is ≈ 63 in.^{3}. The volume of the shorter cylinder is ≈ 82 in.^{3}.

4. The volume of a cylinder is the area of its bottom layer times its height ($\pi r^2 h$) unit cubes.

D. Students might use the work with the two cylinders in parts A–C to reason that the cylinder with the shorter height has the greater volume. Some students may do the calculations because radius is given rather than circumference. You might ask them to show their work. The volume of cylinder 1 is 160π cm^3. The volume of cylinder 2 is 400π cm^3, so cylinder 2 has a greater volume.

E. Students might say that the surface area is the area of the sheet of paper (lateral surface area) plus twice the area of the base.

Note: The volume of the cylinder is greater than the volume of the prisms. As the number of sides increases in the base, the area of the base increases, so the volume increases. The circle has the largest area of all of the bases considered in Problems 3.1 and 3.2.

3.3 Making Cylinders and Prisms From Nets

Goal

- Develop a strategy for finding the surface area of a cylinder

In this problem, students cut out a net for a cylinder and explore surface area. The goal is to find an efficient strategy or rule for finding the surface area of a cylinder.

Launch 3.3

One possible launch is to challenge students to design a net for a cylinder before you use the student text or distribute the labsheet. You can do this formally, as in the following description, or informally by simply holding up a cylinder and asking students to sketch a net for it. At this stage, students will often make the rectangle forming the lateral surface far too short, as pictured below left. Discuss this as you hand out Labsheet 3.3B.

Lateral surface too short **Lateral surface correct length (π times the diameter)**

If you decide to have students make a more careful version of a net, you will still hold up a cylinder or prism.

- *What would a net for this cylinder look like?*

- *What information do you need to make a net for this cylinder? How would you use that information?*

- *How is the length around the base related to the rectangular part of a net?* (The length of the rectangular part of the net is the same as the circumference of the base.)

Distribute a cylinder (such as juice-concentrate cans or cardboard rolls from paper towels or toilet paper) and grid paper to each pair of students. Paper towel rolls can be easily cut apart to reveal the lateral side which is a rectangle.

- *Make whatever measurements you think you need to design a net that could be used to make a copy of your cylinder.*

If students have difficulty, suggest that they start with the base of the cylinder. They can draw around the cylinder to make the circles for the top and bottom. You may have to give them hints about how to draw the lateral surface. They could put a mark on the rim of the cylinder, then roll the cylinder one complete revolution. Some may want to cut out a sheet of paper to wrap around the cylinder and trace around it on their grid paper.

When everyone has successfully constructed a net for a cylinder, launch the problem.

- *On the labsheet, I will give you a net for another cylinder. You will be working in the reverse direction, making a cylinder and prisms from the pattern.*

The class can work in pairs or small groups, but each student should cut out his or her own nets.

Explore 3.3

Suggested Questions As you circulate, ask questions about what students are doing.

- *What role does each of these three shapes—the two circles and the rectangle—play in making the cylinder?*

- *What are the dimensions of the circle?*

- *What are the dimensions of the rectangle?*

- *How are these dimensions helpful for finding the surface area of the cylinder?*

If needed, repeat these questions for the prisms.

Summarize 3.3

Display some of the cylinders the class explored in the launch activity and let students share their strategies for designing the nets. Then, talk about the nets on the labsheet.

- *Can someone describe how this pattern folds into a cylinder? (Prism?) Does this cylinder (prism) have only one possible net?*

Students should realize from the launch that the patterns can look different, but contain the same two circles and rectangle, corresponding to the ends and the lateral surface.

Ask the class to summarize how to find the surface area of a cylinder. Students should now see that the surface area of a cylinder can be found by adding the area of the lateral surface (which is a rectangle) to the area of the two circular ends. The area of the lateral surface is the height of the cylinder multiplied by the circumference of the base. The area of each circular end is πr^2. To calculate the surface area of a cylinder, some students may go back to the net.

Suggested Questions A similar strategy works for finding the surface area of a prism. Ask questions to get at their understanding of surface area of prisms.

- *How is the net for a prism like that for a cylinder?* (It has two identical circular ends and a rectangle.)

- *So what do you need to know to find the surface area of a prism?* (the area of the base and the area of the rectangle in the net)

- *For which prisms will it be easy to find the area of the base?* (Answers will vary. Possible answer: Rectangular and triangular prisms, because we have formulas for finding their areas; other prisms we have to count and estimate.)

Next, discuss how to find the volume of a cylinder.

- *You found that the base of a cylinder is a circle.*

- *How did you find the number of cubes in the bottom layer?* (by counting squares or using formulas)

- *How did you use this information to find the volume of your cylinder?* (by multiplying this by the height of the cylinder)

- *Suppose we measured the volume of the cylinder using a larger unit cube. How would this affect the number we get for the volume?* (The number would be smaller.)

- *Suppose we measured the volume using a smaller unit cube. How would this affect the number we get for the volume?* (The number would be greater, but the volume is the same. The difference is the answer is more exact.)

- *Sometimes we need to measure a cylinder to describe it or to compute other measures. What ways can you measure a cylinder so that you can describe it to someone else?* (You can measure the height, the circumference, and the diameter or radius of the base.)

- *How much information would you need to give about a cylinder to be sure that someone else could duplicate the cylinder?* (the height and one of these three measures: the radius, the diameter, or the circumference of the base.)

The dimensions for a cylinder are the height and radius (or diameter) of the base. For prisms, the height is necessary and some description of the base. If the base is a regular polygon, then the number of sides and the side length of the polygon can be given.

Depending on your students' needs, you can lead a similar discussion for the volume and surface area of a prism.

Check for Understanding

1. *Consider a cylinder with a radius of 2 centimeters and a height of 4 centimeters. Describe how you could design a net for this cylinder.* (They can first determine the circumference and then use the measurements to draw the circles and the rectangle.)

2. For an interesting demonstration that focuses on estimating the height of a circular object, hold up a cylindrical tennis ball container.

- *Which is greater: the circumference of this can or its height?* (Use a piece of string to demonstrate that the circumference is greater.)

- *Which is greater: the distance around your knee or the distance around your neck?* (Have students use their hands to determine the answer. Again, they will probably be surprised.)

3. *The height of a cylindrical can is 10 cm, and the radius of its base is 3 cm. Estimate the volume and surface area of the can, using the fact that π is a little more than 3.* [First, find the area of the base. $\pi \times 3^2 = 9\pi$, or about 28 cm^2. Use this information to find the volume. 10 cm $\times$ 28 cm^2, or about 280 cm^3. The surface area is the sum of the areas of the top and bottom, plus the area of the side. Area of top = area of bottom = 28 cm^2. The area of the side is the circumference of the base times the height. The circumference of the base is $2\pi \times 3$ cm = 6π cm, or about 19 cm. So, the area of the side is 10 cm $\times$ 19 cm, or 190 cm^2. The total area is $2(28$ cm$^2) + 190$ cm^2, or about 246 cm^2.]

3.3 Making Cylinders and Prisms From Nets

Mathematical Goal

- Develop a strategy for finding the surface area of a cylinder

Launch

Challenge students to design a net for a cylinder before you use the student text or distribute the labsheet.

- *What would a net for this cylinder look like?*
- *What information do you need to make a net for this cylinder?*
- *How would you use that information?*

Distribute a cylinder (such as juice-concentrate cans or cardboard rolls from paper towels or toilet paper) and grid paper to each pair of students.

- *Make whatever measurements you think you need to design a net that could be used to make a copy of your cylinder.*

If students have difficulty, suggest that they start with the base of the cylinder. They can draw around the cylinder to create the circles for the top and bottom. When everyone has successfully constructed a net for a cylinder, launch the problem.

- *On the labsheet is a net for another cylinder. You will be working in the reverse direction, making a cylinder and prisms from the pattern.*

The class can work in pairs or small groups on this problem, but each student should cut out his or her own nets.

Materials
- Labsheets 3.3A and 3.3B
- Scissors
- Tape
- Cm grid paper
- Transparencies 3.3A and 3.3 B

Explore

As you circulate, ask questions about what students are doing.

- *What role does each of these three shapes—the two circles and the rectangle—play in making the cylinder?*
- *What are the dimensions of the circle?*
- *What are the dimensions of the rectangle?*
- *How are these dimensions helpful for finding the surface area of the cylinder?*

If needed, repeat these questions for the prisms.

Summarize

Display some of the cylinders the class explored in the launch activity, and let students share their strategies for designing the nets.

Ask the class to summarize how to find the surface area of a cylinder. A similar strategy works for finding the surface area of a prism. Ask questions to get at their understanding of the surface area of prisms.

Materials
- Student notebooks

continued on next page

- *How is the net for a prism like that for a cylinder?*
- *So what do you need to know to find the surface area of a prism?*
- *For which prisms will it be easy to find the area of the base?*

Next, discuss how to find the volume of a cylinder.

Depending on your students' needs, you can lead a similar discussion for the volume and surface area of a prism.

ACE Assignment Guide for Problem 3.3

Core 15–17

Other *Connections* 31, 32; unassigned choices from previous problems

Adapted For suggestions about adapting ACE exercises, see the CMP *Special Needs Handbook*. **Connecting to Prior Units** 31–32: *Bits and Pieces II*

Answers to Problem 3.3

A. Triangular prism: 97.5 cm^2

Pentagonal prism: 90 cm^2

Cylinder: 132.55 cm^2

Possible explanation: I found the area of the base, doubled this, then added the result to the area of the large rectangle that wraps around the prism (cylinder).

B. 1. As above, find the area of the base. There are two bases, so this can be doubled. Then find the area of the rectangle that wraps around the prism (cylinder). Add these two results for the total surface area. Note: The ways to find the area of the base and the rectangle for each prism and the cylinder are different.

2. Instead of estimating the area of the base by counting the square units, you use the dimension of the base to compute the area. The volume is the area of the base times height. **Note:** At this level students only have a formula for finding areas of triangles, rectangles, and circles.

C. 1. Find the area of the base (by a formula or estimation). Then multiply this by the height of the prism (cylinder).

Triangular prism: 37.5 cm cubes

Pentagonal prism: 60 cm cubes

Cylinder: 113 cm cubes

Cylinder: radius = 3 cm and height = 4 cm

2. The volume of a prism and a cylinder could be measured by finding the area of the base and then multiplying it by the height.

Goals

- Apply understanding of volume to solve problems

- Understand that a variety of different three-dimensional figures can have the same volume but different surface areas

In this problem, students apply their knowledge of finding volumes and surface areas of cylinders and rectangular prisms.

Launch 3.4

Tell the story of how Fruit Tree juice company wants to package individual juice drinks in rectangular boxes with the same volume as the cylindrical cans they are currently using.

- *What information will you need to design the rectangular box?*

- *Can we use the same dimensions as the cylinder? Why or why not?*

As an alternate way to present the problem, bring in a juice can and ask the class to find its volume and then to design a rectangular container with the same volume. Or, display a rectangular juice container and ask the class to design a cylindrical can with an equal volume.

Distribute centimeter grid paper, and have each student design a juice box.

Let each student design his or her own box and then move into groups of 2–3 to compare the designs.

Explore 3.4

Allow students time to discuss and design their boxes in small groups.

Suggested Questions First, they will need to find the volume of the juice can (approximately 100.5 cm^3). Ask questions such as the following:

- *How do you find the volume of a rectangular prism?* (area of the base × height)

- *If you plan for a particular base for a volume of 100.5 cubic units, how can you find a height to go with it?* (Divide the area of the base into 100.5 to find the number of layers, which equals the height.)

- *If I make a base that's 3 centimeters by 4 centimeters, what height would I need?* (About 8.4 centimeters)

Students will use different levels of accuracy. Some will be ready for the kind of thinking displayed above. Others will simply estimate their way to something close (for example, a box with a volume of 100 cm^3).

Going Further You might challenge students to design an innovative container that is not a rectangular prism; a triangular prism, for instance, or a cylinder different from the original yet with the same volume.

Summarize 3.4

Look for a variety of rectangular boxes. Ask students how they decided on the dimensions of their boxes. Here are some explanations students have offered:

David: *"I decided to make the bottom of the box a 4-centimeter square. So, the area of the base is 16 centimeters. That means the height had to be 100.5 ÷ 16 = about 6.28 centimeters."*

Trisha: *"I wanted my box to be 8 centimeters high, just like the can, so the base had to be 100.5 ÷ 8 = 12.6 square centimeters. If one side of the base is 3 centimeters, the other side has to be 12.6 ÷ 3 = 4.2 centimeters."*

Leng: *"I found three numbers that multiply to give 100.5, 4 × 5 × 5.025 = 100.5, and made these the dimensions of my box."*

Help the class compare the boxes they made.

- *Which of these boxes do you think would be easiest to drink from?*

- *Which do you think would cost the least to manufacture?*

- *Which would be the easiest to pack in a larger shipping box?*

By this time, students should have a general strategy for finding the volume and surface area of a rectangular prism and of a cylinder. To assess their knowledge, give them a specific problem to work on in class. For example:

- *A box of rice has dimensions, in centimeters, of 4 by 16 by 20. What are the dimensions of a cylinder that would hold the same amount of rice?* (The volume of the box is 1,280 cm^3. If we choose a radius of 5 cm for the cylindrical container, the base will have an area of about 78.5 cm^2, so we need a height of 16.3 cm.)

- *How do the surface areas of the two containers compare?* [The surface area of the box is $2(4 \times 16) + 2(4 \times 20) + 2(16 \times 20) = 928$ cm^2. The surface area of the cylinder described above is $2(78.5) + 16.3 \times 31.4 = 669$ cm^2. The cylinder requires about 259 cm^2 less material.]

3.4 Making a New Juice Container

Mathematical Goals

- Apply understanding of volume to solve problems
- Understand that a variety of different three-dimensional figures can have the same volume but different surface areas

Launch

Tell the story of how Fruit Tree juice company wants to package individual juice drinks in rectangular boxes with the same volume as the cylindrical cans they are currently using.

- *What information will you need to design the rectangular box?*
- *Can we use the same dimensions as the cylinder? Why or why not?*

Distribute centimeter grid paper and have each student design a juice box.

Materials
- Juice can and/or juice box (optional)
- Cm grid paper
- Colored pencils or markers
- Tape
- Scissors

Explore

Allow students time to discuss and design their boxes in small groups.

Ask questions such as the following:

- *How do you find the volume of a rectangular prism?*
- *If you plan for a particular base, how can you find a height to go with it?*
- *If I make a base that's 3 centimeters by 4 centimeters, what height would I need?*

Students will use different levels of accuracy. Some will be ready for the kind of thinking displayed above. Others will simply estimate their way to something close.

Summarize

Look for a variety of rectangular boxes. Ask students how they decided on the dimensions of their boxes.

Help the class compare the boxes they made.

- *Which of these boxes do you think would be easiest to drink from?*
- *Which do you think would cost the least to manufacture?*
- *Which would be the easiest to pack in a larger shipping box?*

To assess students' knowledge, give them a specific problem to work on in class. For example:

- *A box of rice has dimensions, in centimeters, of 4 by 16 by 20. What are the dimensions of a cylinder that would hold the same amount of rice?*
- *How do the surface areas of the two containers compare?*

Materials
- Student notebooks

Core 18, 20–22
Other *Applications* 19; *Extensions* 33–35; unassigned choices from previous problems

Adapted For suggestions about adapting Exercise 22 and other ACE exercises, see the CMP *Special Needs Handbook*.

Answers to Problem 3.4

A. 1. Answers will vary. In particular, students' level of accuracy will vary. Possible nets for boxes with a volume of 100.8 cm^3 (the can has a volume of $\approx$ 100.53 cm^3):

2. Answers will vary based on nets in Question A.

3. Answers will vary.

B. Answers will vary. For the nets in Question A, we have surface areas of 152.4 cm^2 and 158.4 cm^2. The surface area of the cylindrical can is about 125.6 cm^2.

The student edition pages for this
investigation begin on the next page.

Notes

Prisms and Cylinders

In Investigation 2, you found the volume of rectangular prisms by filling the prism with cubes. The number of cubes in the bottom layer is the same as the area of the rectangular base and the number of layers is the height. To find the volume, you multiply the area of the base ($\ell \times w$) times its height h, so that $V = \ell wh$.

A **prism** is a three-dimensional shape with a top and a base that are congruent polygons, and *lateral* (side) faces that are parallelograms. Each prism is named for the shape of its base. The boxes we have seen so far in this unit are rectangular prisms. A triangular prism has a triangular base.

A **cylinder** is a three-dimensional shape with a top and base that are congruent circles.

The prisms and cylinder below all have the same height.

Suppose you filled the triangular prism with rice and poured the rice into each of the other cylinders. How do you think the volumes would compare? What about the surface areas?

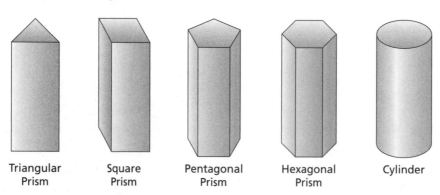

| Triangular Prism | Square Prism | Pentagonal Prism | Hexagonal Prism | Cylinder |

3.1 Filling Fancy Boxes

In this problem you will explore prisms with bases that are not rectangles. You will start by making models of prisms.

Notes _____

_____

_____

_____

Directions for Making Paper Prisms (These paper models are open at the top and bottom.)

- Start with four identical sheets of paper.
- Use the shorter dimension as the height for each prism.
- Make a *triangular* prism by marking and folding one of the sheets of paper into three congruent rectangles. Tape the paper into the shape of a triangular prism.

Triangular Prism

- Make a *square* prism by marking, folding, and taping a sheet of paper into four congruent rectangles.
- Make a *pentagonal* prism by marking, folding, and taping a sheet of paper into five congruent rectangles.
- Make a *hexagonal* prism by marking, folding, and taping a sheet of paper into six congruent rectangles.

Problem 3.1 Finding the Volumes of Other Prisms

A. In your group, follow the directions above. (Keep your models for Problem 3.2.)

B. How do the volumes of the prisms compare as the number of faces in the prisms increases? Does the volume remain the same? Explain.

C. Consider the number of cubes you need to cover the base as one layer. Next, think about the total number of layers of cubes needed to fill the prism. Does this seem like a reasonable method for computing the volume of each prism?

D. Suppose that each of your paper prisms has a top and a bottom. As the number of faces of a prism (with the same height) increases, what happens to the surface area of the prisms? Are the surface areas of the prisms the same? Explain your reasoning.

ACE Homework starts on page 38.

STUDENT PAGE

Notes _____

_____

_____

_____

3.2 Filling Cylinders

The last problem revealed some interesting connections among volume and surface area of prisms. A cylinder resembles a many-sided prism. In this problem you will explore cylinders and use what you have already learned about prisms to find the volume and surface area of a cylinder.

Directions for Making Paper Cylinders

- Start with two identical sheets of paper.
- Use the longer dimension of one sheet of paper as the height of the first cylinder. Tape the paper into the shape of a cylinder.
- Use the shorter dimension of the other sheet of paper as the height of the second cylinder. Tape the paper into the shape of a cylinder.

How do the volumes of the two cylinders compare?

You need an efficient way to compute the volume of a cylinder. In Problem 3.1 you found the volume of a prism by counting the number of cubes that fit in a single layer at the base and then counting the number of layers it would take to fill the prism. Let's see if a similar approach will work for cylinders.

| Trace the base. | How many cubes would fit in one layer? | How many layers would it take to fill the cylinder? |

As with rectangular prisms, the bottom of any prism or cylinder is called the base.

Notes

_____

_____

_____

_____

Problem 3.2 Finding the Volumes of Cylinders

A. Copy the circles at the right onto inch graph paper. With two identical sheets of paper, make two models of cylinders with open tops and bases that match the bases drawn on the grid paper.

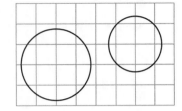

active math online

For: Virtual Cylinder Activity
Visit: PHSchool.com
Web Code: and-6302

B. Predict which of the two cylinders has the greater volume.

C. 1. How many inch cubes fit on the bottom layer of each cylinder?

   2. How many layers of inch cubes are needed to fill each cylinder?

   3. What is the total number of inch cubes needed to fill each cylinder?

   4. How can the dimensions help you calculate the volume of each cylinder?

D. Suppose Cylinder 1 has a height of 10 centimeters and a radius of 4 centimeters and Cylinder 2 has a height of 4 centimeters and a radius of 10 centimeters. Are the volumes equal? Explain.

E. Suppose that each of your paper cylinders had a top and a bottom. Describe how you could find the surface area of each cylinder.

ACE Homework starts on page 38.

3.3 Making Cylinders and Prisms from Nets

The distance from the base of a cylinder to the top is called the height. You can describe a cylinder by giving its dimensions.

radius

height

base

Notes _____

_____

_____

_____

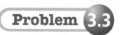

Problem 3.3 **Finding the Surface Area of Cylinders and Prisms**

Draw nets like the following on centimeter grid paper.

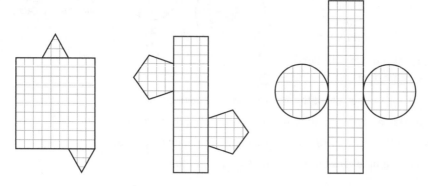

A. What is the surface area of each shape? Explain your reasoning.

B. Cut out your nets. Tape the pieces of the nets together to form a cylinder or a prism.

   1. Describe how to find the surface area of any prism or cylinder.

   2. Describe how the dimensions of a cylinder help you to find its surface area.

C. 1. Find the volume of each prism and cylinder.

   2. Compare the methods for finding the volume of a prism and finding the volume of a cylinder.

ACE Homework starts on page 38.

The volume, or capacity, of a liquid container is often given in units like quarts, gallons, liters, and milliliters. These volumes do not tell you how many unit cubes each container will hold, but are based on cubic measures. For example, a gallon equals 231 cubic inches, a milliliter equals a cubic centimeter, and a liter is 1,000 cubic centimeters.

Go **O**nline
PHSchool.com
For: Information about capacities
Web Code: ane-9031

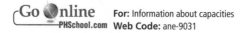

Notes _____

_____

_____

_____

3.4 Making a New Juice Container

active math online

For: Pouring and Filling Activity
Visit: PHSchool.com
Web Code: and-6304

Fruit Tree Juice Company packages its most popular drink, apple-prune juice, in cylindrical cans. Each can is 8 centimeters high and has a radius of 2 centimeters.

Recent reports indicate a decline in the sales of Fruit Tree juice. At the same time, sales of juice sold by a competitor, the Wrinkled Prune Company, are on the rise. Market researchers at Fruit Tree determine that Wrinkled Prune's success is due to its new rectangular juice boxes. Fruit Tree decides to package its juice in rectangular boxes.

Problem 3.4 Comparing Volumes

Fruit Tree wants the new rectangular box to have the same volume as the current cylindrical can.

A. 1. On centimeter grid paper, make a net for a box that will hold the same amount of juice as the cylindrical can. Cut out your net. When you are finished, fold and tape your pattern to form a rectangular box.

2. Give the dimensions of your juice box. Are there other possibilities for the dimensions? Explain.

3. Compare your juice box with the boxes made by your classmates. Which rectangular box shape do you think would make the best juice container? Why?

B. Compare the surface area of the cylindrical can with the surface area of your juice box. Which container has greater surface area?

ACE Homework starts on page 38.

Notes _____

_____

_____

_____

Applications

1. Cut a sheet of paper in half so you have two identical half-sheets of paper. Tape the long sides of one sheet together to form a cylinder. Tape the short sides from the second sheet together to form another cylinder. Suppose that each cylinder has a top and a bottom.

   a. Which cylinder has the greater volume? Explain.

   b. Which cylinder has the greater surface area? Explain.

2. A cylinder has a radius of 3 centimeters. Sand is poured into the cylinder to form a layer 1 centimeter deep.

   a. What is the volume of sand in the cylinder?

   b. Suppose the height of the cylinder is 20 centimeters. How many 1-centimeter deep layers of sand are needed to fill the cylinder?

   c. What is the volume of the cylinder?

3. Find a cylindrical object in your home or school. Record the dimensions and find the volume of the cylinder.

Notes _____

_____

_____

_____

For Exercises 4–6, decide whether you have found an area, a surface area, or a volume. Then, identify whether the computation relates to Figure 1, 2, or 3.

4. $\left(\frac{1}{2} \times \frac{1}{2} \times \pi \times 2\right) + \left(2 \times \frac{1}{2} \times \pi \times 5\right)$

5. $3 \times 3 \times \pi$

6. $1 \times 1 \times \pi \times 3$

1 cm

3 cm

Figure 1

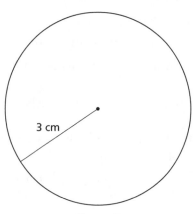
$\frac{1}{2}$ cm

5 cm

3 cm

Figure 2

3 cm

Figure 3

7. A pipeline carrying oil is 5,000 kilometers long and has an inside diameter of 20 centimeters.

   a. How many cubic centimeters of oil will it take to fill 1 kilometer of the pipeline? (1 km = 100,000 cm)

   b. How many cubic centimeters of oil will it take to fill the entire pipeline?

Homework
Help Online
PHSchool.com
For: Help with Exercise 7
Web Code: ane-6307

Investigation 3 Prisms and Cylinders **39**

Notes _____

_____

_____

_____

8. What feature of a cylinder uses the given units?

   a. centimeters

   b. square centimeters

   c. cubic centimeters

For Exercises 9–11, find the volume of each cylinder.

Go Online
PHSchool.com

For: Multiple-Choice Skills Practice

Web Code: ana-6354

  9. height = 10 centimeters, radius = 6.5 centimeters

10. height = 6.5 centimeters, radius = 10 centimeters

11. height = 12 inches, area of the base = 200 square inches

12. Find the surface area of each closed cylinder in Exercises 9 and 10.

13. a. Will all rectangular prisms with the same height and base area have the same shape? Explain.

   b. Will all cylinders with the same height and base area have the same shape? Explain.

14. A cylindrical storage tank has a radius of 15 feet and a height of 30 feet.

   a. Make a sketch of the tank and label its dimensions.

   b. Find the volume of the tank.

   c. Find the surface area of the tank.

15. a. Sketch two different prisms, each with a base of area 40 square centimeters and a height of 5 centimeters.

   b. Find the volumes of your prisms.

   c. Do you think everyone in your class drew the same prisms? Explain.

   d. Do you think all the prisms have the same volumes as your prisms? Explain.

40   Filling and Wrapping

Notes _____

_____

_____

_____

16. Below are side and top views of a triangular prism with bases that are equilateral triangles.

   a. What is the volume of this prism? How did you find the volume?

   b. What is the surface area? How did you find the surface area?

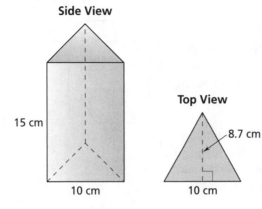

Side View

15 cm

10 cm

Top View

8.7 cm

10 cm

17. Below is a scale model of a net for a cylinder.

☐ = 1 square cm

   a. Suppose the net is assembled. Find the volume of the cylinder.

   b. Find the surface area of the cylinder.

18. Which container below has the greater volume? Greater surface area?

A *closed rectangular prism* whose height is 12 centimeters, width is 3 centimeters, and length is 4 centimeters.

A *closed cylinder* whose height is 12 centimeters and diameter is 3 centimeters.

Investigation 3 Prisms and Cylinders   **41**

Notes _____

_____

_____

_____

19. The bases of the prisms you made in Problem 3.1 are shown at the right. Each prism has a height of 8.5 inches.

1 inch × 1 inch grid

   a. Compute the volume of each prism.

   b. Compare these volumes with those you found in Problem 3.1.

20. Carlos wants to build a circular hot tub with a volume of 1,000 cubic feet. What is a good approximation for the radius of the tub?

21. Carlos decides he would rather build a rectangular hot tub that is 4 feet high and holds 400 cubic feet of water. What could the dimensions of the base of Carlos's hot tub be?

22. A popcorn vendor needs to order popcorn boxes. The vendor must decide between a cylindrical box and a rectangular box.

- The cylindrical box has a height of 20 centimeters and a radius of 7 centimeters.

- The rectangular box has a height of 20 centimeters and a square base with 12-centimeter sides.

- The price of each box is based on the amount of material needed to make the box.

- The vendor plans to charge $2.75 for popcorn, regardless of the shape of the box.

   a. Make a sketch of each box. Label the dimensions.

   b. Find the volume and surface area of each box.

   c. Which box would you choose? Give the reasons for your choice. What additional information might help you make a better decision?

42   Filling and Wrapping

Notes _____

_____

_____

_____

Connections

23. Serge and Jorge were talking about the number π. Serge said that any problem involving π had to be about circles. Jorge disagreed and showed him the example below. What do you think?

1 inch

π inches

24. The Buy-and-Go Mart sells drinks in three sizes. Which size gives the most ounces of drink per dollar? Explain.

Small	Medium	Large
12 oz.	18 oz.	32 oz.
$1.25	$1.75	$3.00

25. a. Identify objects at school that are shaped like prisms, one rectangular and one or two non-rectangular prisms.

   b. Without measuring, estimate the volume of each object.

   c. How can you check the volumes you found in part (b)?

26. A drink can is a cylinder with radius 3 centimeters and height 12 centimeters. Ms. Doyle's classroom is 6 meters wide, 8 meters long, and 3 meters high. Estimate the number of drink cans that would fit inside Ms. Doyle's classroom. Explain your estimate.

Investigation 3 Prisms and Cylinders   **43**

Notes _____

_____

_____

_____

27. a. Make a table showing the relationship between the diameter and the circumference of a circle. Include data for diameters 1, 2, 3, . . . 10 centimeters. Use this table for parts (b)–(d).

b. Graph the data in your table.

c. Suppose that each of the circles represented in your table is the base of a cylinder with height of 2 centimeters. Some of these cylinders are sketched below. Make a table to show the relationship between the diameter of the base and the volume of the cylinder.

d. Make a graph of the volume data.

e. Compare the graphs of parts (b) and (d). How are they alike? How are they different?

28. Some take-out drink containers have a circular top and bottom that are not congruent. How can you estimate the volume of the container below?

29. Leo has two prism-shaped containers. One has a volume of $3\frac{3}{4}$ cubic feet and the other has a volume of $\frac{1}{3}$ cubic feet.

a. How many of the smaller prisms would it take to fill the larger prism?

b. What operation did you use to find the answer? Explain.

30. Emily has two prism-shaped containers. One has a volume of $2\frac{2}{5}$ cubic feet, and the other has a volume of $\frac{2}{3}$ cubic feet.

a. How many of the smaller prisms would it take to fill the larger prism?

b. What operation did you use to find the answer? Explain.

Notes _____

_____

_____

_____

31. The diagram shows a fish tank after a container of water is poured into the tank.

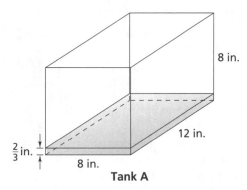

8 in.

12 in.

$\frac{2}{3}$ in.

8 in.

Tank A

a. How many containers of water are needed to fill the tank?

b. What fraction of the tank does the container fill?

c. A different container holds $12\frac{3}{4}$ cubic inches of water. How many of these containers are needed to fill the tank?

32. The diagram shows a fish tank after a container of water is poured into the tank.

4 in.

15 in.

$1\frac{3}{5}$ in.

5 in.

Tank B

a. How many containers of water are needed to fill the tank?

b. What fraction of the tank does the container fill?

c. A different container holds $4\frac{4}{9}$ cubic inches of water. How many of these containers are needed to fill the tank?

Investigation 3 Prisms and Cylinders **45**

Notes _____

_____

_____

_____

Extensions

33. A cylindrical can is packed securely in a box as shown at the right.

   a. Find the radius and height of the can.

   b. What is the volume of the empty space between the can and the box?

   c. Find the ratio of the volume of the can to the volume of the box.

   d. Make up a similar example with a can and a box of different sizes. What is the ratio of the volume of your can to the volume of your box? How does the ratio compare with the ratio you found in part (c)?

10 cm

2 cm

34. a. The drawing at the right shows a prism with an odd-shaped top and bottom and rectangular sides. The top and bottom each have an area of 10 square centimeters, and the height is 4 centimeters. What is the volume of the prism? Explain your reasoning.

   b. Is your estimate for the volume more than, less than, or equal to the exact volume? Explain.

35. Suppose you know the height and volume of a cylinder. Can you make a net for the cylinder?

Notes _____

_____

_____

_____

Mathematical Reflections 3

In this investigation, you developed methods for finding the volume and surface area of prisms and cylinders. These questions will help you summarize what you have learned.

Think about your answers to these questions. Discuss your ideas with other students and your teacher. Then write a summary of your findings in your notebook.

1. Describe how to find the volume of a rectangular prism.

2. **a.** Describe how you can find the volume of a cylinder using its dimensions. Write a rule that represents your strategy.

   b. Describe how you can find the surface area of a cylinder using its dimensions. Write a rule that represents your strategy.

3. Discuss the similarities and differences in the methods for finding the volume of a cylinder, a rectangular prism, and a non-rectangular prism.

4. Discuss the similarities and differences in the methods for finding the surface area of a cylinder, a rectangular prism, and a non-rectangular prism.

Notes _____

_____

_____

Investigation 3

ACE
Assignment Choices

Differentiated Instruction
Solutions for All Learners

Problem 3.1
Core 1
Other *Connections* 23–25

Problem 3.2
Core 2, 8–12, 26
Other *Applications* 3–7, 13–14; *Connections* 27–30; unassigned choices from previous problems

Problem 3.3
Core 15–17
Other *Connections* 31, 32; unassigned choices from previous problems

Problem 3.4
Core 18, 20–22
Other *Applications* 19; *Extensions* 33–35; unassigned choices from previous problems

Adapted For suggestions about adapting Exercise 22 and other ACE exercises, see the CMP *Special Needs Handbook.*
Connecting to Prior Units 23: *Covering and Surrounding*; 24: *Comparing and Scaling*; 27: *Variables and Patterns*; 29–32: *Bits and Pieces II*

Applications

NOTE: All answers were computed using 3.14 for π.

1. **a.** The cylinder made by taping the short sides together will have the greater volume (31.63 cm^3 vs. 20.47 cm^3). One way to think about this is that the radius gets squared in finding volume, so we want to make this as big as possible (see the following note). However, at this stage students have not mastered any strategy for finding the volume of a cylinder. So they may focus incorrectly on height.

b. If we imagine that the cylinders have tops and bottoms, then the cylinder made by taping together the short sides will have a larger top and bottom than the other cylinder. Since the area of the paper is the same for the two cylinders, the shorter cylinder has the greater surface area.

For the Teacher Regardless of the size paper we begin with, the shorter cylinder will always have the greater surface area. A small amount of algebra shows this: If ℓ is the length of our sheet of paper and w is the width, then the radius of our cylinder will be: $\ell \div 2\pi$. So the volume, after some computation, is: $(\ell^2 w) \div 4\pi$. Putting the larger value in for ℓ will maximize the volume. Your students will not produce this level of justification, but some may be curious if it is always true.

2. **a.** approximately 28.26 cm^3 or 9π cm
   b. 20 layers
   c. approximately 565.2 cm^3 or 180π cm^3

3. Answers will vary.

4. 5.5π or 17.27. This is the surface area, in sq. cm, of Figure 2.

5. 9π or 28.26. This is the area, in sq. cm, of Figure 3.

6. 3π. This is the volume for Figure 1.

7. **a.** approximately 31,400,000 cm^3
   b. approximately 157,000,000,000 cm^3 (5,000 times as much)

8. **a.** height, radius, diameter, and circumference of the base
   b. area of the base and surface area
   c. volume

9. $6.5 \times 6.5 \times \pi \times 10 \approx 1{,}326.65$ cm^3

10. $10 \times 10 \times \pi \times 6.5 \approx 2{,}041$ cm^3

11. $200 \times 12 = 2{,}400$ in.^{3}.

12. For the cylinder in Exercise 9, surface area $=$ $(6.5 \times 6.5 \times \pi \times 2 + 2 \times 6.5 \times \pi \times 10) \approx 673.53$ cm^2

For the cylinder in Exercise 10, surface area $=$ $(10 \times 10 \times \pi \times 2 + 2 \times 10 \times \pi \times 6.5) \approx 1{,}036.2$ cm^2

13. a. No, because prisms with the same area of the base may have different dimensions for their bases. For example, an area of 24 cm^2 could be 2 by 12 or 4 by 6 for length and width.

b. Yes, because the same area of the base means their radii are the same.

14. a. Possible sketch:

30 ft

15 ft

b. approximately 21,195 ft^3

c. approximately 4,239 ft^2

15. a. Possible sketch:

5 cm   10 cm

4 cm

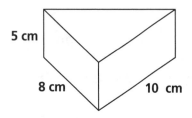

5 cm

8 cm   10 cm

b. All such prisms, regardless of shape, will have a volume of 200 cm^3.

c. Probably not. Many such prisms are possible because there are many polygons with an area of 40 cm^2.

d. Yes, all correct prisms will have a volume of 200 cm^3. This is because we can think of the area of the base being one layer of unit cubes and the height being the number of identical layers required to fill the prism. Then the volume is the product of the area of the base and the height. These are both given in this problem.

16. a. 652.5 units^3. The area of the base is 43.5 sq. units. Multiply this by the height.

b. 537 units^2. Each rectangle has an area of 150 sq. units. Each triangle has an area of 43.5 sq. units. So, $3 \times 150 + 2 \times 43.5 = 537$.

17. a. approximately 169.6 cm^3 or 54π cm^3

b. approximately 169.6 cm^2 using formula, or 170.55 using net for rectangular part

18. The prism has both greater volume and surface area. (Volume of prism and cylinder: 144 cm^3, 84.8 cm^3. Surface area of prism and cylinder: 192 cm^2, 127.2 cm^2)

19. a. Triangular prism: about 49.9 cubic inches, $\dfrac{3.67 \times 3.2}{2} \times 8.5$

Square prism: about 64.28 cubic inches, $2.75 \times 2.75 \times 8.5$

Pentagonal prism: 70.55 cubic inches, 8.3×8.5

Hexagonal prism: about 74.3 cubic inches, $(1.83 \times 3.2 + 3.2 \times 0.9) \times 8.5$

b. These volumes are similar to those in Problem 3.1.

20. Answers may vary. Possible answer: if height is 4 feet, then the base area is 250 square feet and the radius is approximately 8.9 feet.

21. The area of the base needs to be 100 ft^2. One such base is 10 ft by 10 ft.

22. a.

b. Cylindrical box: volume is approximately 3,077.2 cm³, surface area is approximately 1,033.06 cm². (Note: Being popcorn boxes, these do not have tops.)

Rectangular box: volume is 2,880 cm³. Surface area is 1,104 cm².

c. Answers will vary. The cylindrical box will hold more popcorn. As a manager, you might choose the rectangular box because you will be going through less popcorn. However, its surface area is slightly more than the cylinder, which may increase the cost of the box, so the costs may offset each other.

Connections

23. Jorge is correct. The area of this rectangle is π. (The point here is that π is a real number.)

For the Teacher Students may struggle with this problem because they are unused to thinking of π as a length. Instead they, like Serge in the problem, think of π as a number useful in problems about circles. Nonetheless, π is a number that can theoretically designate a length just as easily as 2 can.

24. The large size is the best buy. For $1.00, you would get about 10.67 oz with the large size, about 10.3 oz with the medium size, or about 9.6 oz with the small size.

25. a. Answers will vary.

b. Answers will vary.

c. Measure to find the area of the base. Measure the height and multiply this by the area of the base.

26. If the cans are packed as though they were rectangular (Figure 1), 13,300 cans would cover the floor in one layer. 25 layers will fill the room for a total of 332,500 cans.

If the cans are packed more efficiently (Figure 2), more cans could fit in each layer.

Figure 1 **Figure 2**

27. a.

Circle Relationships

Diameter (cm)	Circumference (cm)
1	3.14
2	6.28
3	9.42
4	12.56
5	15.7
6	18.84
7	21.98
8	25.12
9	28.26
10	31.4

b.

Circle Relationships

c.

Cylinders With 2-cm Heights

Diameter (cm)	Volume (cm³)
1	1.57
2	6.28
3	14.13
4	25.12
5	39.25
6	56.52
7	76.93
8	100.48
9	127.17
10	157

d.

Cylinders With 2-cm Heights

e. Both graphs are increasing. As the diameter increases, the volume increases. However, the first graph is a straight line indicating that the rate of change is fixed from x to $x + 1$. In the second graph, the rate of change from one value of the diameter to the next in the table is not fixed. In fact, the volume grows faster in this graph as the diameter increases.

28. The container's volume should be between the volumes of the large and the small cylinders with radius 4.5 and 3, or between 890.19 and 395.64. In fact, it should be around the middle value of 890.19 and 395.64,

respectively, which is 642.92. Another way to find its volume is to find the difference between the cones with radius 4.5 and 3. The height of the small cone could be found by using the proportion of the container's difference of radii and height, which is $\frac{1.5}{14} = \frac{3}{x}$. Then $x = 28$. The container's volume is the difference of the two cones, which is $890.19 - 263.76 = 626.43$ cm³.

29. **a.** $3\frac{3}{4} \div \frac{1}{3} = 11\frac{1}{4}$ of the small containers to fill the larger.

    b. Division. Because the question asks how many one-thirds are in three and a third.

30. **a.** $2\frac{2}{5} \div \frac{2}{3} = 3\frac{3}{5}$ of the small containers to fill the larger.

    b. Division. Because the question asks how many two-thirds are in two and two-fifths.

31. **a.** $8 \div \frac{2}{3} = 12$ containers

    b. $\frac{1}{12}$ of the volume of the tank

    c. a little more than 60 containers

32. **a.** $4 \div 1\frac{3}{5} = \frac{5}{2}$ or $2\frac{1}{2}$ containers

    b. $\frac{2}{5}$ of the volume of the tank

    c. $300 \div 4\frac{4}{9} = 67\frac{1}{2}$ containers

Extensions

33. **a.** Radius: 1 cm

    Height: 10 cm

    b. Approximately 8.6 cm³, the difference between the volume of the box (40 cm³) and the volume of the can (≈ 31.4 cm³).

    c. about 0.785 (Formally, it would be π to 4.)

    d. Specific answers will vary. However, for any such can and box, the ratio will be as in Question C. This is because the volume of the box is $(2r)^2 \times h$ while the volume of the can is $\pi r^2 \times h$. So, the ratio becomes $\pi r^2 h$ to $4r^2 h$, or π to 4.

34. **a.** The volume of this prism, as for any other prism, is found by multiplying the area of the base by the height. Here, this is 40 cm³.

    b. Exact volume

35. To make a net of a cylinder, we must know its radius and height. Because we know the height and volume of a cylinder, by the formula $V = \pi r^2 h$, we can find the radius by dividing V by $\pi \times h$ and then find its square root.

Possible Answers to Mathematical Reflections

1. The volume of a rectangular prism can be found by multiplying the number of cubes that would fit in the bottom layer of the prism by the number of layers that would fit in the prism. Or, it can be found by multiplying the area of the base by the height of the prism or by multiplying length by width by height; $V = \ell \times w \times h$.

2. a. The volume of a cylinder can be found by multiplying the area of its base by the height of the cylinder. Because the base is a circle, the area of the base is πr^2. The height of the cylinder can be represented by h. Thus, the volume of a cylinder can be found by using $V = \pi r^2 h$.

b. The surface area of a cylinder can be found by finding the sum of the area of the two circular ends, $2\pi r^2$ and then the area of the lateral surface and adding them together. The lateral surface is a rectangle, with its length the circumference of the circular base, $2\pi r$, and the width of the rectangle is the height of the cylinder. Thus, the surface area of the cylinder can be represented by: $SA = 2\pi r^2 + 2\pi rh$.

3. For rectangular prisms and cylinders, the volume is the area of the base times the height. For prisms with bases that are polygons, finding the area depends on what kind of polygon it is. For cylinders, the base is always a circle for which we have a formula that gives us the area.

4. For surface area, you have to find the areas of all parts of a net that will cover the prism or cylinder. A cylinder always has a simple net made up of a square or rectangle and two circles. Prisms have more faces to consider—2 identical bases plus the lateral faces.

Investigation 4 Cones, Spheres, and Pyramids

Mathematical and Problem-Solving Goals

- Explore a volume relationship between cylinders and spheres

- Extend students' understanding of volume as layering to other ways of filling a three-dimensional figure

- Explore a volume relationship between cylinders, cones and spheres

- Explore a volume relationship between pyramids and prisms

- Strengthen understanding of the volume relationships among cones, spheres, and cylinders and between prisms and pyramids

- Use the relationships among cylinders, cones, and spheres to develop a strategy for finding the volume of a cone or sphere

- Use the relationship between prisms and pyramids to develop a strategy for finding the volume of a pyramid

Summary of Problems

Problem 4.1 Comparing Spheres and Cylinders

Students compare the volumes of a sphere and a cylinder by manipulating modeling clay.

Problem 4.2 Cones and Cylinders, Pyramids and Cubes

Students compare the volumes of a cone and a cylinder to develop a formula for the volume of a cone. They repeat the experiment to compare the volumes of a pyramid and a prism to develop a formula for the volume of a pyramid.

Problem 4.3 Melting Ice Cream

Students compare the volumes of cones, cylinders, and spheres in an application problem.

	Suggested Pacing	Materials for Students	Materials for Teachers	ACE Assignments
All	$4\frac{1}{2}$ days			
4.1	$1\frac{1}{2}$ days	Modeling dough; transparent plastic; scissors; tape; Labsheet 4.1	Transparencies 4.1A and 4.1B; sample spheres and cylinders—see Teacher Note	1–8, 26, 27, 32, 34
4.2	$1\frac{1}{2}$ days	Stiff paper; scissors; tape; sand or rice cylinders made in 4.1; Labsheets 4.2A–E	Transparency 4.2; cylinders; plastic models of a cone and cylinder with the same radius and height (optional); plastic models of a prism and pyramid with the same base and height (optional)	9–16, 28, 33, 37
4.3	1 day		Transparency 4.3; ice cream cone and cylindrical cup (optional)	17–25, 29–31, 35, 36
MR	$\frac{1}{2}$ day			

4.1 Comparing Spheres and Cylinders

Goals

- Explore a volume relationship between cylinders and spheres

- Extend students' understanding of volume as layering to other ways of filling a three-dimensional figure

This problem is intended to help students develop a visual image of the relationship between the volume of a sphere and the volume of a cylinder. Often, formulas are given to students with little or no justification. This hands-on experiment will give students experiences in which they may explore the reasonableness of the formula for finding volume of a sphere.

A Comment on Experiment or Demonstration

It is more effective if students have the opportunity to experiment on their own, but some teachers use Problems 4.1 and 4.2 as a demonstration to save time. If you choose to conduct the experiments as a class demonstration, try to create more than one example, and leave the containers on display so students can experiment with them later. We have provided a centimeter grid, Labsheet 4.1, that helps with making the cylinders.

You may want to purchase commercially available transparent containers (often sold in mathematics-supply catalogs and stores), which can be filled with colored water or sand and used to explore volume relationships.

As a demonstration, some teachers have had success using a tennis ball and creating a cylinder, with an open top and bottom, that matches the height and diameter of the tennis ball. Place the cylinder on a piece of paper, and put the ball into the cylinder. Pour sand into the cylinder, shaking it gently so that the sand settles in the empty space around the ball. Carefully lift the ball out of the cylinder and measure the volume the sand occupies. It will be about one-third the volume of the cylinder, which means the sphere occupied two-thirds of the cylinder. In this problem, modeling clay is used to make a sphere.

Launch 4.1

Suggested Questions Hold up one of your sample cylinders.

- *How might you find the volume of this cylinder?* (Possible answer: By thinking of layers, each with a volume equal to the area of the base of the cylinder.)

Hold up a sphere with a diameter equal to the height of the cylinder.

- *How do you think the volumes of these two solids compare?* (The volume of the cylinder is larger.)

- *How do you know?* (Possible answer: The sphere will fit inside the cylinder with space left over.)

- *How much larger do you suppose the volume of the cylinder is than the volume of the sphere? Is it twice as large? More? Less?*

After students make their guesses, talk to them about the experiment in Problem 4.1.

Distribute modeling dough (vary the amount so the spheres students create will be of different sizes) and a strip of transparent plastic to each group.

Students can work in small groups of 2 to 3.

Explore 4.1

As groups work on the problem, make sure their spheres and cylinders have the same diameters and heights.

If students follow the directions for the experiment carefully, they will find that the flattened sphere occupies about two thirds of the cylinder, indicating that the sphere's volume is $\frac{2}{3}$ of the cylinder's volume.

Summarize 4.1

Ask groups to share what they discovered about the relationship of a sphere's volume to a cylinder's volume. It should be clear from their measurements that the sphere's volume is about two-thirds the cylinder's volume. You may want to help students notate their verbal expression with something like this:

Volume of sphere = $\frac{2}{3}$ · Volume of cylinder

Some students, however, may be able to write this relationship as a formula:

Volume of sphere = $\frac{2}{3} \cdot \pi r^2(h)$

Some might be ready to understand that as the height of the sphere is twice its radius, $2r$ may be substituted for h (You may have to remind students what r^2 and r^3 mean or just write them as $r \cdot r$ or $r \cdot r \cdot r$):

Volume of sphere = $\frac{2}{3} \cdot \pi r^2(2r) = \frac{4}{3}\pi r^3$

If some students focus on the relationship between the height of the empty space and the height of the sphere—saying that the height of the empty space is half the height of the flattened sphere—affirm this and help them refocus on comparing the measures to the cylinder. The height of the flattened sphere is two-thirds the height of the cylinder, and the height of the empty space is one-third the height of the cylinder.

Help students form a visual image of the relationship between a cylinder's volume and a sphere's volume by using an illustration like the one below. To find the sphere's volume, students can visualize a cylinder with the same height and radius as the sphere, find the volume of the cylinder, and take two-thirds of it.

To find the volume of a sphere,

start by thinking of a cylinder with the same radius and height.

Students will probably see the formula for the volume of a sphere, $\frac{4}{3}\pi r^3$, in books, so it may be worth talking about how the $\frac{2}{3}$ they found becomes $\frac{4}{3}$. Remember that $h = 2r$ in this instance. Then, volume of sphere = $\frac{2}{3}\pi r^2(h) = \frac{2}{3}\pi r^2(2r) = \frac{4}{3}\pi r^3$

Suggested Question Offer another example to assess students' understanding.

- *What is the volume of a sphere that has a radius of 5 centimeters?*

Going Further As an extension activity for students who seem to have a good grasp of the relationship between the volumes of spheres and cylinders, have students estimate the amount of empty space in a cylindrical tennis ball container with three tennis balls inside.

The height of the container is equal to three times the diameter of a tennis ball, and the diameter of the container equals that of a tennis ball. Thus, the volume of the container is $3(2r)(\pi r^2) = 6\pi r^3$. The volume of a tennis ball is $\frac{4}{3}\pi r^3$, so three tennis balls have a volume of $3(\frac{4}{3}\pi r^3) = 4\pi r^3$. This means that the empty space is $2\pi r^3$. (Don't push for this much symbolic representation if you have students do this problem. Their work will likely be a series of multiplication problems, which is fine at this stage.)

In the next problem, students will need the cylinders they have made in this problem.

Another interesting visualization task is to ask students which is greater—the height of the tennis can or the circumference? (The circumference is greater. Use a string to visually demonstrate this.)

4.1 Comparing Spheres and Cylinders

Mathematical Goals

- Explore a volume relationship between cylinders and spheres
- Extend students' understanding of volume as layering to other ways of filling a three-dimensional figure

Launch

Hold up one of your sample cylinders.

- *How might you find the volume of this cylinder?*

Hold up a sphere with a similar diameter.

- *How do you think the volumes of these two solids compare? How do you know? How much larger do you suppose the volume of the cylinder is than the volume of the sphere? Is it twice as large? More? Less?*

After students make their guesses, talk to them about the experiment in Problem 4.1.

Materials

- Transparencies 4.1A and 4.1B
- Sample spheres and cylinders
- Labsheet 4.1 (optional)

Explore

Distribute modeling dough (vary the amount so the spheres students create will be of different sizes) and a strip of transparent plastic to each group of two or three students. (Be sure that one has a diameter close to 6 cm and keep it for Problem 4.2.)

As groups work on the problem, make sure that they create spheres and that the cylinders they make are very close in diameter to their spheres.

If students follow the directions for the experiment carefully, they will find that the flattened sphere occupies about $\frac{2}{3}$ of the cylinder, indicating that the sphere's volume is $\frac{2}{3}$ of the cylinder's volume.

Materials

- Modeling dough
- Strips of transparent plastic
- Tape

Vocabulary

- cone
- pyramid
- sphere

Summarize

Ask groups to share what they discovered about the relationship of a sphere's volume to a cylinder's volume. You may want to help students notate their verbal expression symbolically.

If some students focus on the relationship between the height of the empty space and the height of the sphere—saying that the height of the empty space is half the height of the flattened sphere—affirm this and help them refocus on comparing the measures to the cylinder. The height of the flattened sphere is two-thirds the height of the cylinder, and the height of the empty space is one-third the height of the cylinder.

Help students form a visual image of the relationship between a cylinder's volume and a sphere's volume by using an illustration.

Offer another example to assess students' understanding.

- *What is the volume of a sphere that has a radius of 5 centimeters?*

Materials

- Student notebooks

ACE Assignment Guide for Problem 4.1

Core 1, 3–8
Other *Applications* 2; *Connections* 26, 27, 32; *Extensions* 34

Adapted For suggestions about adapting ACE exercises, see the CMP *Special Needs Handbook*.
Connecting to Prior Units 27: *Data About Us*

Answers to Problem 4.1

A. Answers will vary. Example: Height of cylinder: 7.5 cm, height of empty space: 2.5 cm, and height of flattened sphere: 5 cm.

B. Using the clay, the volume of the sphere should be about $\frac{2}{3}$ of the volume of the cylinder when they have the same radius and height.

C. $\frac{2}{3}$ of 48 in.^{3} is 32 in.^{3}.

Goals

- Explore and use a volume relationship between cylinders, cones, and spheres

- Explore and use a volume relationship between prisms and pyramids to find the volume of a pyramid

Students will conduct an experiment to explore the relationship between the volume of a cone and the volume of a cylinder. They construct a cone with the same radius and height as the cylinder they made in Problem 4.1 (see the student edition and Transparency 4.2). Then, they use the cone to fill the cylinder with sand or rice. We have provided nets for two sizes of cylinders and cones and one set of a pyramid and prism as Labsheets 4.2A–E. In the sets, we have provided a cylinder with diameter and height 6 cm and a cube with dimensions 6 cm × 6 cm × 6 cm. We have also provided a net for a cone and for a pyramid that will fit the cylinder and the cube for the two experiments.

To save time, this could be conducted as a demonstration, but students will develop a greater understanding of cones if they make one and do the filling themselves. If your district does not require students to know the volume of a pyramid, you can omit Question E.

Launch 4.2

Talk about the experiments in Problem 4.2 and distribute sand or rice to each group. Distribute Labsheets 4.2A–E if you choose to use them.

Students can work in groups of 2 to 3 to first experiment with the cylinder/cone volume relationship and then with the prism/pyramid volume relationship.

Explore 4.2

Have students work in their groups to construct a cone and then compare the volumes of the cone and the cylinder.

Be aware that some students will struggle to make their cones. You may need to help them do so, or to pair students appropriately to provide for this.

As groups explore the problem, help those who are having trouble making a cone or trimming it down to the height of their cylinder. An alternative is to provide the nets on Labsheets 4.2A–C.

It may be difficult for students to make a square pyramid without using Labsheet 4.2E.

Summarize 4.2

Ask groups to share what they learned about the relationship of a cone's volume to a cylinder's volume.

It takes three cones full of sand or rice to fill the cylinder. Students should be able to explain this relationship in words: for a cone and a cylinder of the same height and radius, the volume of the cone is one-third the volume of the cylinder. You may want to help students notate this:

Volume of cone = $\frac{1}{3}$ · volume of cylinder

Some students may be able to write this relationship as a formula:

Volume of a cone = $\frac{1}{3}\pi r^2 h$, or $\frac{2}{3}\pi r^3$

(Remember that $h = 2r$ in this experiment.)

Clear plastic containers are great for demonstrating this relationship and will help students develop a visual image of it. You can also help students to see this relationship by using an illustration like the one below.

To find the volume of a cone,   **start by thinking of a cylinder with the same radius and height (in this case, twice the radius).**

Suggested Question Offer another example to assess their understanding.

- *What is the volume of a cone with a radius of 5 centimeters and a height of 10 centimeters?* (about 261.67 cm^3)

- *What is the volume of a pyramid with a 10 cm-by-10 cm base and a height of 10 cm?* (about 333.33 cm^3)

Put models from the two experiments up in front of the class and discuss the relationship across the three shapes.

- *Describe how you can find the volume of a sphere. Of a cone.*

- *What information do you need? In what ways did you use your knowledge of cylinders to find the volume?*

Repeat the discussion questions with the prism and the pyramid noting that the relationship is the same; the volume of a pyramid is $\frac{1}{3}$ the volume of the prism with the same base and height.

Suggested Question

- *Suppose you know the dimensions of the base and height of a rectangular prism, how might you find the volume of the pyramid?* (It is similar to finding the volume of a square pyramid. The volume is $\frac{1}{3}$ the area of the base times the height.)

Check for Understanding

A cone, cylinder, and sphere all have a radius of 4 cm. The height of the cylinder and cone is 6 cm.

- *What is the volume of each?* (cylinder $\approx$ 301.6 cm^3; cone $\approx$ 100.5 cm^3; and sphere $\approx$ 201.1 cm^3)
- *Find the volume of a cone whose height is 4 cm and whose radius is 3 cm.* ($\approx$ 37.7 cm^3)

- *Find the volume of a sphere whose radius is 3 cm.* ($\approx$ 113.04 cm^3)

- *Find the volume of a square pyramid whose height is 7 cm and whose base has sides of 4 cm.* ($\frac{1}{3} \cdot 4 \cdot 4 \cdot 7 \approx$ 37.33 cm^3)

Going Further ACE Exercise 37, which asks students to think about pyramids, makes a nice extension for the summary. As the number of sides in the base of a pyramid increases, the shape of the pyramid approaches that of a cone. The volume of a pyramid is found the same way the volume of a cone is found.

4.2 Cones and Cylinders, Pyramids and Cubes

Mathematical Goals

- Explore and use a volume relationship between cylinders, cones and spheres
- Explore and use a volume relationship between prisms and pyramids to find the volume of a pyramid

Launch

Talk about the experiment in Problem 4.2 and distribute sand or rice to each group. If you choose to use the nets from Labsheets 4.2A–E distribute those.

Materials
- Sand or rice
- Transparent cylinders from 4.1
- Labsheets 4.2A–E
- Scissors and tape
- Stiff blank paper
- Transparency 4.2

Explore

Have students work in their groups to construct a cone and then compare the volumes of the cone and the cylinder.

Be aware that some students will struggle to make their cones. You may need to help them do so, or to pair students appropriately to provide for this. Use the labsheets to help.

As groups explore the problem, help those who are having trouble making a cone or trimming it down to the height of their cylinder.

Have students repeat the experiment with the prism and pyramid nets provided. Ask questions about how these two kinds of objects—cones and cylinders and pyramids and prisms—are alike and different.

Materials
- Clear plastic models of a prism and pyramid with same height and base (optional)

Summarize

Ask groups to share what they learned about the relationship of a cone's volume to a cylinder's volume.

It takes three cones full of sand or rice to fill the cylinder. Students should be able to explain this relationship in words: for a cone and a cylinder of the same height and radius, the volume of the cone is one-third the volume of the cylinder. You may help students notate this symbolically. Repeat the questions for the pyramid and prism. The relationship is the same.

Some students may be able to write these relationships as formulas.

Clear plastic containers are great for demonstrating these relationships and will help students develop visual images of them. You can also help students to see this relationship by using an illustration.

Materials
- Student notebooks
- Clear plastic models of a cone and cylinder with same height and radius (optional)

continued on next page

Offer another example to assess their understanding.

- *What is the volume of a cone with a radius of 5 centimeters and a height of 10 centimeters? A pyramid with a 10 cm-by-10 cm base and a height of 10 cm?*

ACE Assignment Guide for Problem 4.2

Core 9–14
Other *Applications* 15–16, *Connections* 28, *Extensions* 33, 37; unassigned choices from previous problems

Adapted For suggestions about adapting Exercise 11 and other ACE exercises, see the CMP *Special Needs Handbook*.
Connecting to Prior Units 28: *Data About Us*

Answers to Problem 4.2

A. Using the rice, the volume of a cone should be about $\frac{1}{3}$ of the volume of the cylinder.

B. The cone's volume is $\frac{1}{3}$ of the cylinder's volume, and the sphere's volume is $\frac{2}{3}$ of the cylinder's volume. Therefore, the cone's volume is $\frac{1}{2}$ of the sphere's volume. Some students may notice that the volumes of the sphere and cone together will exactly fill the cylinder. Some may be able to write the relationships as formulas:
volume of cylinder $= \pi r^2 h$;
volume of sphere $= \frac{2}{3}\pi r^2 r = \frac{2}{3}\pi r^2(2r) = \frac{4}{3}\pi r^3$;
volume of cone $= \frac{1}{3}\pi r^2 r = \frac{1}{3}\pi r^2(2r) = \frac{2}{3}\pi r^3$.

C. 1. The sphere's volume would be $\frac{2}{3}$ of the cylinder's volume ($42\frac{2}{3}$ in.^{3}).

2. The cone's volume would be $\frac{1}{3}$ of the cylinder's volume ($21\frac{1}{3}$ in.^{3}).

D. The volume of the cylinder would be approximately 628 cm^3, the volume of the cone would be approximately 209 cm^3, and the volume of the sphere would be approximately 523 cm^3.

E. 1. Using the rice, the volume of a pyramid should be about $\frac{1}{3}$ of the volume of the prism.

2. The volumes of the cones and pyramids are both $\frac{1}{3}$ of the volume of a cylinder or the prism.

4.3 Melting Ice Cream

Goals

- Strengthen understanding of the volume relationships among cones, spheres, and cylinders
- Use the relationships among cylinders, cones, and spheres to develop a strategy for finding the volume of a cone or sphere

In this problem, students use their new knowledge about volume to explore whether the volume of a sphere will fill a cone or a cylinder with the same dimensions. This is a short problem and could be assigned as homework after Problem 4.2.

Launch 4.3

If you decide to do this problem in class, tell the story of Esther and Jasmine's trip to the ice cream parlor. Make sure students understand that the ice cream melts into the containers.

Although the problem is designed to have students use what they already know to make comparisons, a demonstration may still be useful—if you don't mind ice cream melting in your classroom! Such an experiment would also raise the issue of whether the volume of the ice cream will remain the same as it melts. A science teacher may be able to help coordinate an experiment to enhance students' mathematics work.

Have students work on the problem individually and check answers in pairs.

Explore 4.3

For students who are struggling, ask how this problem is similar to Problems 4.1 and 4.2 and how it is different from them. Guide a discussion that helps them see how to apply what they have learned about volume to this problem.

Summarize 4.3

Have students share their conclusions and reasoning.

Some will reason from the relationships they found in Problems 4.1 and 4.2; some may calculate the volumes of all three shapes and compare them. Be sure both ideas are presented.

From their explanations, you will be able to assess their understanding of the volumes of cones, spheres, and cylinders.

Discuss students' answers to Question C. Most will understand that the cone holds only half of a scoop. It may take more discussion to help all students understand that the cylinder holds one and a half scoops.

Check for Understanding
Hold up a sphere.

- *The radius of the sphere is 7 cm. Describe a method for finding its volume.*

Hold up a cylinder.

- *The radius of the cylinder is 4 cm and its height is 7 cm. Describe a method for finding its volume.*

4.3 Melting Ice Cream

Mathematical Goals

- Strengthen understanding of the volume relationships among cones, spheres and cylinders
- Use the relationships among cylinders, cones, and spheres to develop a strategy for finding the volume of a cone or sphere

Launch

If you decide to do this problem in class, tell the story of Esther and Jasmine's trip to the ice cream parlor. Make sure students understand that the ice cream melts into the containers.

Although the problem is designed to have students use what they already know to make comparisons, a demonstration may still be useful—if you don't mind ice cream melting in your classroom! Such an experiment would also raise the issue of whether the volume of the ice cream will remain the same as it melts. A science teacher may be able to help coordinate an experiment to enhance students' mathematics work.

Materials
- Transparency 4.3
- Ice cream cone (optional)
- Cylindrical cup (optional)

Explore

Have students work on the problem individually and check answers in pairs.

For students who are struggling, ask how this problem is similar to Problems 4.1 and 4.2 and how it is different from them. Guide a discussion that helps them see how to apply what they have learned about volume to this problem.

Summarize

Have students share their conclusions and reasoning.

Some will reason from the relationships they found in Problems 4.1 and 4.2; some may calculate the volumes of all three shapes and compare them. Be sure both ideas are presented.

From their explanations, you will be able to assess their understanding of the volumes of cones, spheres, and cylinders.

Discuss students' answers to Question C. Most will understand that the cone holds only half of a scoop. It may take more discussion to help all students understand that the cylinder holds one and a half scoops.

Materials
- Student notebooks

ACE Assignment Guide
for Problem 4.3

Core 17–22, 25
Other *Applications* 23, 24, *Connections* 29–31, *Extensions* 35, 36; unassigned choices from previous problems

Adapted For suggestions about adapting ACE exercises, see the CMP *Special Needs Handbook*.

Answers to Problem 4.3

A. The cylindrical cup has a volume of $\pi \times 4^2 \times 8$ or about 402 cm^3. The spherical scoop of ice cream has $\frac{2}{3}$ of the cylinder's volume, or about 268 cm^3. If the ice cream melts, it will not completely fill the cup.

B. The cone has the same height and radius as the cup, so its volume is $\frac{1}{3}$ the cup's volume, or about 134 cm^3. The ice cream has twice this volume, so, if it melts, it will overflow the cone.

C. The cup will hold about 402 cm^3 of ice cream; the cone will hold about 134 cm^3 of ice cream. Because one scoop of ice cream has a volume of about 268 cm^3, half a scoop will pack into the cone, and one and a half scoops will pack into the cup.

The student edition pages for this investigation begin on the next page.

Notes _____

_____

_____

_____

Cones, Spheres, and Pyramids

Many common and important three-dimensional objects are not shaped like prisms or cylinders. For example, ice cream is often served in **cones.** The planet we live on is nearly a **sphere.** Many monuments here and in other countries are shaped like **pyramids.**

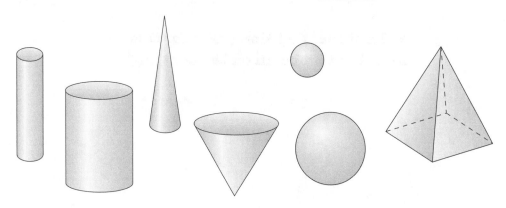

As with a cylinder and a prism, you can describe a cone or a square pyramid by giving its dimensions. The dimensions of a cone are the radius of its circular base and its height. The dimensions of a square pyramid are its length, width, and height.

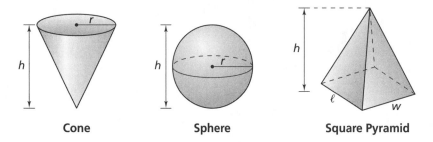

| Cone | Sphere | Square Pyramid |

Although spheres may differ in size, they are all the same shape. You can describe a sphere by giving its radius.

In this investigation, you will explore ways to determine the volumes of cones, pyramids, and spheres by looking for relationships between cones and pyramids and between cones and spheres.

Notes _____

_____

_____

_____

4.1 Comparing Spheres and Cylinders

In this problem, you will make a sphere and a cylinder with the same diameter and the same height and then compare their volumes. (The height of a sphere is just its diameter.) You can use the relationship you observe to develop a method for finding the volume of a sphere.

Earth is nearly a sphere. You may have heard that, until Christopher Columbus's voyage in 1492, most people believed Earth was flat. Actually, as early as the fourth century B.C., scientists had figured out that Earth was round.

The scientists observed the shadow of Earth as it passed across the moon during a lunar eclipse. The shadow was round. Combining this observation with evidence gathered from observing constellations, these scientists concluded that Earth was spherical. In the third century B.C., Eratosthenes, a Greek mathematician, was actually able to estimate the circumference of Earth.

Go Online
PHSchool.com **For:** Information about historical views of Earth's shape **Web Code:** ane-9031

Problem 4.1 Comparing Spheres and Cylinders

- Make a sphere from modeling clay. Measure its diameter.
- Make a cylinder with an open top and bottom from a sheet of stiff transparent plastic to fit snugly around your clay sphere. Trim the height of the cylinder to match the height of the sphere. This makes the diameter and the height of the cylinder equal to the diameter and the height of the sphere. Tape the cylinder together so that it remains rigid.

Notes _____

_____

_____

_____

● Now, flatten the clay sphere so that it fits snugly in the bottom of the cylinder. Mark the height of the flattened sphere on the cylinder.

height of cylinder

open top

height of empty space

height of flattened sphere

A. Measure and record the height of the cylinder, the height of the empty space, and the height of the flattened sphere. Use this information to find the volume of the cylinder and the original sphere.

B. What is the relationship between the volume of the sphere and the volume of the cylinder?

C. A cylinder with a height equal to its diameter has a volume of 48 cubic inches. How can you use the relationship in Question B to find the volume of a sphere whose radius is the same as the cylinder?

Remove the clay from the cylinder and save the cylinder for Problem 4.2.

ACE Homework starts on page 54.

4.2 Cones and Cylinders, Pyramids and Cubes

In Problem 4.1, you discovered the relationship between the volume of a sphere and the volume of a cylinder. In this problem, you will look for the relationship between the volume of a cone and the volume of a cylinder, and between the volume of a pyramid and the volume of a square prism.

Notes _____

_____

_____

_____

- Roll a piece of stiff paper into a cone shape so that the tip touches the bottom of the cylinder you made in Problem 4.1.

- Tape the cone shape along the seam. Trim the cone so that it is the same height as the cylinder.

- Fill the cone to the top with sand or rice, and empty the contents into the cylinder. Repeat this as many times as needed to fill the cylinder completely.

A. What is the relationship between the volume of the cone and the volume of the cylinder?

B. Suppose a cylinder, a cone, and a sphere have the same radius and the same height. What is the relationship between the volumes of the three shapes?

C. Suppose a cone, a cylinder, and a sphere all have the same height, and that the cylinder has a volume of 64 cubic inches. How do you use the relationship in Question B to find

   1. the volume of a sphere whose radius is the same as the cylinder?

   2. the volume of a cone whose radius is the same as the cylinder?

D. Suppose the radius of a cylinder, a cone, and a sphere is 5 centimeters and the height of the cylinder and cone is 8 centimeters. Find the volume of the cylinder, cone, and sphere.

Investigation 4 Cones, Spheres, and Pyramids   **51**

Notes _____

_____

_____

_____

E. 1. Use a square prism and a pyramid to conduct an experiment similar to the one on the previous page. The pyramid should have the same size base as the prism and the same height (shown at the right).

What is the relationship between the volume of the prism and the volume of the pyramid.

2. How are finding the volumes of the cones and pyramids alike?

 Homework starts on page 54.

4.3 Melting Ice Cream

Esther and Jasmine buy ice cream from Chilly's Ice Cream Parlor. They want to bring back an ice cream cone to Esther's little brother but decide the ice cream would melt before they got back home. Jasmine wonders, "If the ice cream all melts into the cone, will it fill the cone?"

Problem 4.3 Comparing Volumes of Spheres, Cylinders, and Cones

Esther gets a scoop of ice cream in a cone, and Jasmine gets a scoop in a cylindrical cup. Each container has a height of 8 centimeters and a radius of 4 centimeters. Each scoop of ice cream is a sphere with a radius of 4 centimeters.

A. Suppose Jasmine allows her ice cream to melt. Will the melted ice cream fill her cup exactly? Explain.

52 Filling and Wrapping

Notes _____

_____

_____

_____

B. Suppose Esther allows her ice cream to melt. Will the melted ice cream fill her cone exactly? Explain.

C. How many same-sized scoops of ice cream of the size shown on the previous page can be packed into each container?

ACE Homework starts on page 54.

Frank and Ernest

© 2002 Thaves. Reprinted with permission. Newspaper dist. by NEA, Inc.

Did You Know?

You have looked at prisms, cylinders, cones, and spheres. Many three-dimensional objects do not have such regular shapes.

According to legend, Archimedes (ahr kuh MEE deez) made an important discovery while taking a bath in the third century B.C. He noticed that the water level rose when he sat down in a tub. This was because his body had *displaced* some water. He determined that he could find the weight of any floating object by finding the weight of the water that the object displaced.

It is said that Archimedes was so excited about his discovery that he jumped from his bath and, without dressing, ran into the streets shouting "Eureka!"

Go Online
PHSchool.com
For: Information about water displacement
Web Code: ane-9031

STUDENT PAGE

STUDENT PAGE

Notes _____

_____

_____

_____

Applications

1. A playground ball has a diameter of 18 cm.

   a. Sketch a cylinder that fits the playground ball, and label its height and base.

   b. What is the volume of the cylinder?

   c. What is the volume of the ball?

2. Find the volume of an exercise ball with a diameter of 62 centimeters.

For Exercises 3–6, find the volume of the following spheres. In some spheres, the diameter is given. In others, the radius is given.

3.

15 cm

4.

8 cm

5.

6 cm

6.

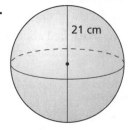

21 cm

For Exercises 7–9, each of the number sentences models the formula for the volume of a figure you have worked with in this unit. Name the figure, sketch and label the figure, and find the volume.

7. $2\frac{2}{3} \times 4\frac{4}{5} \times 3\frac{7}{8}$

8. $\pi \times (2.2)^2 \times 6.5$

9. $\frac{1}{3}\pi \times (4.25)^2 \times 10$

Notes _____

_____

_____

_____

10. Watertown has three water storage tanks in different shapes: a cylinder, a cone, and a sphere. Each tank has a radius of 20 feet and a height of 40 feet.

   a. Sketch each tank, and label its dimensions.

   b. Estimate which tank will hold the most water. Explain.

   c. What is the volume of the cylindrical tank?

   d. What is the volume of the conical tank?

   e. What is the volume of the spherical tank?

11. Find the volume of each shape.

Homework
Help **O**nline
PHSchool.com
For: Help with Exercise 11
Web Code: ane-6411

a.

3 cm
6 cm

b.

3 cm
6 cm

c.

3 cm

d. How do the volumes of the three shapes compare?

For Exercises 12 and 13, find the volume of each shape.

12.

6 cm
5 cm
4 cm

13.

6 cm
5 cm
4 cm

14. a. Sketch and label the dimensions of a pyramid with base dimensions 5 centimeters by 7 centimeters and height 8 centimeters.

   b. Find the volume of the pyramid in part (a).

Notes _____

_____

_____

_____

15. The track-and-field club is planning a frozen yogurt sale to raise money. They need to buy containers to hold the yogurt. They must choose between the cup and the cone below. Each container costs the same. The club plans to charge customers $1.25 for a serving of yogurt. Which container should the club buy? Why?

16. The Mathletes are planning their own frozen yogurt sale. They need to buy containers to hold the yogurt. They must choose between the prism and pyramid below. The other conditions that apply to the club in Exercise 15 also apply to the Mathletes. Which container should the club buy? Why?

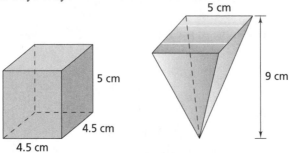

17. The prices and dimensions of several movie theater popcorn containers are shown below. Which container has the most popcorn per dollar? Explain. (Note: The diagrams below are not drawn to scale.)

Notes _____

_____

_____

_____

For Exercises 18–20, the volume of each shape is approximately 250 cubic inches.

18. Find the height of a cylinder with a radius of 3 inches.

19. Find the radius of a sphere.

20. Find the height of a cone with a radius of 3 inches.

For Exercises 21–22, suppose each shape has a square base, the side of the base is 3 inches, and the volume is 225 cubic inches. Find the height.

21. rectangular prism   **22.** pyramid

23. If a scoop of ice cream is a sphere with a radius of 1 inch, how many scoops can be packed into the cone at the right?

1 inch

5 inches

24. Chilly's Ice Cream Parlor purchases ice cream in $2\frac{1}{2}$-gallon cylindrical containers. Each container is $10\frac{5}{32}$ inches high and 9 inches in diameter. A jumbo scoop of ice cream comes in the shape of a sphere that is approximately 4 inches in diameter. How many jumbo scoops can Chilly's serve from one $2\frac{1}{2}$-gallon container of ice cream?

25. Chilly's Ice Cream Parlor is known for its root beer floats.

- The float is made by pouring root beer over 3 scoops of ice cream until the glass is filled $\frac{1}{2}$ inch from the top.
- A glass is in the shape of a cylinder with a radius of $1\frac{1}{4}$ inches and height of $8\frac{1}{2}$ inches.
- Each scoop of ice cream is a sphere with a radius of $1\frac{1}{4}$ inches.

Will there be more ice cream or more root beer in the float? Explain your reasoning.

Investigation 4 Cones, Spheres, and Pyramids   **57**

Notes _____

_____

_____

_____

Connections

26. A drink can is a cylinder with a radius of 3 centimeters and a height of 12 centimeters.

    a. Sketch the can, and label its dimensions.

    b. What is the circumference of the can?

    c. What is the volume?

    d. What is the surface area?

    e. How many cans will it take to fill a liter bottle? (A liter bottle contains 1,000 cubic centimeters.)

27. Three students measured the height of the same cylinder and their measurements are listed below. What is the average of the heights?

$2\frac{1}{2}$ feet $\qquad\qquad$ $2\frac{2}{3}$ feet $\qquad\qquad$ $2\frac{7}{12}$ feet

Go Online
PHSchool.com
For: Multiple-Choice Skills Practice
Web Code: ana-6454

28. Five students measured the height of the same prism and their measurements are listed below. What is the average of the heights?

    5.1 centimeters $\qquad\qquad$ 4.9 centimeters

    5.25 centimeters $\qquad\qquad$ 5.15 centimeters

    4.85 centimeters

Each number sentence in Exercises 29–31 is a model for the surface area of a three-dimensional figure. Identify which three-dimensional figure the number sentence describes. Find the surface area.

29. $2 \times (4) + 2 \times (8.5) + 2 \times (7.25)$

30. $2 \times (4 + 8.5 + 7.25)$

31. $2\pi \times (4)^2 + 2\pi \times (4)(8.5)$

32. Kaiya measures the circumference of a sphere and finds that it is 54 centimeters. What is the volume of the sphere?

Notes _____

_____

_____

_____

Extensions

33. Ted made a scale model of a submarine for his science class.

   a. What is the volume of Ted's model?

   b. If 1 inch in the model represents 20 feet in the actual submarine, what is the volume of the actual submarine?

3 in.

4 in.

3 in.

12 in.

34. Some of the Inuit people build igloos shaped like hemispheres (halves of a sphere). Some of the Hopi people in Arizona build adobes shaped like rectangular boxes. Suppose an igloo has an inner diameter of 20 feet.

   a. Describe the shape of a Hopi dwelling that would provide the same amount of living space as the igloo described above.

   b. What dimensions of the floor would give the Hopi dwelling the same amount of floor space as the igloo?

Investigation 4 Cones, Spheres, and Pyramids   **59**

Notes _____

_____

_____

_____

35. A pyramid is named for the shape of its base. The left shape below is a triangular pyramid, the center shape is a square pyramid, and the right shape is a pentagonal pyramid.

   a. Suppose the bases of a pyramid are all regular polygons. What happens to the shape of the pyramid as the number of sides in the base increases?

   b. Describe a method for finding the surface area of a pyramid.

36. For each shape below, find the dimensions that will most closely fit inside a cubic box with 5-centimeter edges.

   a. sphere   **b.** cylinder   **c.** cone   **d.** pyramid

   e. Does a sphere, a cylinder, or a cone fit best inside the cubic box? That is, for which shape is there the least space between the shape and the box?

37. The edges of a cube measure 10 centimeters. Describe the dimensions of a cylinder and a cone with the same volume as the cube. Explain.

Which shape should I start with?

Notes _____

_____

_____

_____

Mathematical Reflections 4

In this investigation, you studied the relationships between the volumes of a cone, a sphere, and a cylinder with the same radius and height. You also studied the relationship between a square pyramid and a rectangular prism with the same base and height. These questions will help you summarize what you have learned.

Think about your answers to these questions. Discuss your ideas with other students and your teacher. Then write a summary of your findings in your notebook.

1. **a.** If a cone, a cylinder, and a sphere have the same radius and height, describe the relationships among their volumes. Use examples and sketches to illustrate your answer.

   b. If you know the radius of a sphere, how can you find the volume?

   c. If you know the radius and height of a cone, how can you find the volume?

2. **a.** Suppose a square pyramid and a rectangular prism have the same base and height. How do their volumes compare? Use examples and sketches to support your answer.

   b. Suppose you know the dimensions of the base and the height of a rectangular pyramid. How could you find the volume?

3. **a.** How are pyramids and cones alike and different?

   b. How are prisms and cylinders alike and different?

Notes _____

_____

_____

_____

Investigation 4

ACE
Assignment Choices

Differentiated Instruction
Solutions for All Learners

Problem 4.1
Core 1, 3–8
Other *Applications* 2; *Connections* 26, 27, 32; *Extensions* 34

Problem 4.2
Core 9–14
Other *Applications* 15, 16; *Connections* 28; *Extensions* 33, 37; unassigned choices from previous problems

Problem 4.3
Core 17–22, 25
Other *Applications* 23, 24; *Connections* 29–31; *Extensions* 35, 36; unassigned choices from previous problems

Adapted For suggestions about adapting Exercise 11 and other ACE exercises, see the CMP *Special Needs Handbook*.
Connecting to Prior Units 27, 28: *Data About Us*

Applications

1. a.

18 cm

18 cm

b. $\pi \times 9^2 \times 18 \approx 4{,}578.12$ cm^3

c. $\frac{2}{3} \times 4{,}578.12 \approx 3{,}052.08$ cm^3

2. $\frac{2}{3}\pi \times 31^2 \times 62 \approx 124{,}724.99$ cm^3

or $\frac{4}{3}\pi (31^3) \approx 124{,}724.99$

3. about 1,767.15 cm^3

4. about 2,144.66 cm^3

5. about 113.10 cm^3

6. about 4,849.05 cm^3

7. The rectangular prism's volume is $49\frac{3}{5}$ units^3.

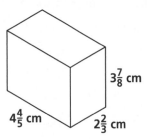

$3\frac{7}{8}$ cm

$4\frac{4}{5}$ cm

$2\frac{2}{3}$ cm

8. The cylinder's volume is about 99 units^3.

2.2 cm

6.5 cm

9. The cone's volume is about 189 units^3.

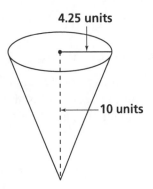

4.25 units

10 units

ACE ANSWERS 4

10. **a.** (Figure 1)

b. The cylindrical tank will hold the most water because the volume of a sphere is $\frac{2}{3}$ the volume of a cylinder with like radius and height dimensions and the volume of a cone is $\frac{1}{3}$ the volume of a cylinder with like radius and height dimensions. Less formally, either the cone or the sphere would fit inside the cylinder with space left over.

c. about 50,265 ft^3

d. $\frac{1}{3} \times 50,265 =$ about 16,755 ft^3

e. $\frac{2}{3} \times 50,265 =$ about 33,510 ft^3

11. **a.** *Cylinder*: about 169.64 cm^3

b. *Cone*: about 56.55 cm^3

c. *Sphere*: about 113.1 cm^3

d. Because all three shapes have the same height and radius, the cylinder's volume is three times the cone's volume and the sphere's volume is twice the cone's volume. Or, the cone's volume is one-third the cylinder's volume and the sphere's volume is two-thirds the cylinder's volume.

12. Volume of prism: $4 \times 5 \times 6 = 120$ cm^3

13. Volume of pyramid: $120 \div 3 = 40$ cm^3

14. **a.**

b. $V = 5 \times 7 \times 8 \div 3 = 93\frac{1}{3}$ cm^3

15. The cylindrical cup holds about 88.4 cm^3 of frozen yogurt; the cone holds about 113 cm^3. If the club wants to raise the most money possible, and they think an equal number of customers will buy the cup as the cone, the club should buy the cup.

16. Prism volume $= 4.5 \times 4.5 \times 5 = 101.25$ cm^3. Pyramid volume $= \frac{1}{3} (5 \times 5 \times 9) = 75$ cm^3. The pyramid is the better choice.

17. The cone container is the best buy because it holds the most popcorn per dollar.

Pyramid: volume $= 1,000$ cm^3; popcorn is $1,000 \div 2.00 = 500$ cm^3 per dollar.

Cone: volume $\approx 3,142$ cm^3; popcorn is $3,142 \div 2.50 \approx 1,257$ cm^3 per dollar.

Cylinder: volume $\approx 4,021$ cm^3; popcorn is $4,021 \div 3.75 \approx 1,072$ cm^3 per dollar.

Box: volume $\approx 3,600$ cm^3; popcorn is $3,600 \div 3.50 \approx 1,029$ cm^3 per dollar.

(NOTE: You may want to discuss with the class what is meant by "best buy." Some students may claim that the one that requires the least packaging material is the best buy. Also, this question asks about the best buy for the customer; ACE Exercises 12–14 concern the best deal for the seller.)

18. 8.85 inches $= \frac{250}{(9 \times \pi)}$

19. 3.91 inches ($r^3 = \frac{2}{3}\pi r^2 h = 250$, where $h = 2r$. So $\frac{2}{3}\pi r^2(2r) = 250$. So $r^3 = 250 \left(\frac{3}{4\pi}\right)$. So $r \approx 3.91$. (Students may find r by guessing a number and multiplying it by itself 3 times.)

20. 26.54 inches $\approx \frac{250}{(3 \times \pi)}$

21. 25 in. **22.** 75 in.

23. Using the relationship between this cone and a cylinder of height 5 inches, the volume of the cone is $\frac{1}{3} \times \pi \times 1^2 \times 5 \approx 5.24$ in.^{3}. Using the relationship between this sphere and a cylinder of height 2 inches, the volume of the scoop is $\frac{2}{3} \times \pi \times 1^2 \times 2 \approx 4.19$ in. It would take $5.24 \div 4.19 \approx 1.25$ scoops to fill the cone. (Or, $\frac{5}{3}\pi \div \frac{4}{3}\pi = \frac{5}{4} = 1.25$ scoops.)

Figure 1

24. The volume of the ice cream container is
$\pi \times (4\frac{1}{2})^2 \times 10\frac{5}{32} \approx 646.11$ cubic inches.
The volume of a jumbo scoop of ice cream is
$\frac{4}{3} \times 8 \times \pi \approx 33.51$ cubic inches. The container
will serve $646.11 \div 33.51 \approx 19.28$, or about
19 jumbo scoops of ice cream.

25. More ice cream; The volume of the glass is
$\pi \times (1.25)^2 \times 8 \approx 39.27$ in.^{3}. The volume of
one scoop of ice cream is $\frac{4}{3} \times \pi \times (1.25)^3 \approx$
8.18 in.^{3}, so 3 scoops have $8.18 \times 3 = 24.54$
in.^{3} of ice cream. Because 24.54 in.^{3} of ice
cream is more than half the volume of the filled
glass, there is more ice cream than root beer.
Alternative solution: The glass is filled to 8 in.
deep. The three scoops of ice cream, sitting
directly on top of each other, will fill $7\frac{1}{2}$ in.,
leaving $\frac{1}{2}$ in. of pure root beer. Each scoop fills
$\frac{2}{3}$ of the part of the glass in which it sits.
Therefore, the ice cream fills $\frac{2}{3}$ of the first
$7\frac{1}{2}$ inches of the glass, which is equivalent to
filling 5 in. of the glass. The remaining 3 in. are
filled with root beer. Thus, there is more ice
cream in the glass than root beer.

Connections

26. a.

3 cm

12 cm

b. $2\pi \times 3 \approx 18.8$ cm
c. $9\pi \times 12 \approx 339$ cm^3

d. The ends each have an area of about
28.3 cm^2 and the lateral surface area has
an area of about 226 cm^2 for a total surface
area of about 283 cm^2.

e. It would take $\frac{1,000}{339} \approx 2.94$ cans or about
3 cans of soda to fill a liter bottle.

27. $(2\frac{1}{2} + 2\frac{2}{3} + 2\frac{7}{12}) \div 3 = 2\frac{7}{12}$ ft

28. $25.25 \div 5 = 5.05$ cm

29. A rectangular or oblique prism with a surface
area of 39.5 units^2.

30. A rectangular or oblique prism with a surface
area of 39.5 units^2. (This is the same prism in
Question A.)

31. A cylinder with a surface area of about
314.16 units^2. [Note: The decimal answer to
this problem, when not approximated, is
exactly 100π. This problem provides an
interesting opportunity to ask students to
show why this happens by solving the
problem in terms of π. $(2 \times \pi \times 4 \times 4)$
$+ (2 \times \pi \times 4 \times 8.5) = 32\pi + 68\pi = 100\pi$.]

32. About 2,664 cm^3. Possible reasoning: Think
of a sphere inside a cylinder. The
circumference of the base would be 54 cm,
giving a radius of $54 \div 2\pi \approx 8.6$ cm. The
height of the cylinder would be twice the
radius, or 17.2 cm. The volume of the cylinder
would be about 3,996 cm^3, so the volume of
the sphere is about $\frac{2}{3} \times 3,996 = 2,664$ cm^3.

Extensions

33. **a.** The submarine is constructed from a
hemisphere, a cylinder, and a cone, so we
must add the volumes of all three.
Hemisphere: $\frac{1}{2} \times \frac{2}{3} \times \pi \times 3^2 \times 6 \approx$
56.5 in.^{3}; cylinder: $\pi \times 3^2 \times 12 \approx$
339.3 in.^{3}; cone: $\frac{1}{3} \times \pi \times 3^2 \times 4 \approx$
37.7 in.^{3}. The total volume is about
$56.5 + 339.3 + 37.7 = 433.5$ in.^{3}.

b. About $433.5 \times 20^3 = 3,468,000$ ft^3

34. **a.** The igloo's volume is $\frac{1}{2} \times \frac{2}{3} \times \pi(10^2)$
$\times 20 \approx 2,094$ ft^3. Possible answer: If the Hopi
make an adobe with a 20-ft-square base, it
would have to be $2,094 \div 400 \approx 5.2$ ft high
to have the same volume as the igloo.
However, because many people are taller
than 5.2 ft, it may make more sense to have a
17-ft-square base with a height of about 7.2 ft
to have about the same volume as the igloo.

b. The igloo has $\pi(10^2) \approx 314$ ft^2 of floor
space. The dimensions of the adobe's
rectangular floor would have to be
multiplied to give 314, for example, 20 ft by
about 15.7 ft. (An infinite number of
dimensions will work, including a square
base of about 17.72 ft by 17.72 ft.)

35. a. As the number of sides in the base increases, the pyramid looks more and more like a cone (assuming regular polygons for the base).

   b. The surface area can be found by adding the areas of the triangles (finding the area of one triangle and multiplying by the number of triangles) to the area of the base.

36. a. A sphere with radius 2.5 cm

   b. A cylinder with radius 2.5 cm, height 5 cm

   c. A cone with radius 2.5 cm and height 5 cm

   d. A base of 5 cm × 5 cm and a height of 5 cm

   e. The cylinder has the least amount of wasted space because it has the largest volume.

37. Answers will vary. Possible answer: the cube has a volume of 1,000 cm^3. A cylinder with a radius of 5 cm has a base area of about 78.5 cm^2 and would need a height of 1,000 ÷ 78.5 ≈ 12.7 cm. A cone with the same base would need three times the height, or about 38.1 cm, to have the same volume.

Possible Answers to Mathematical Reflections

Note: In reading students' answers, if you are unsure of how well they understand these ideas, you might give them the dimensions of some cones, cylinders, and spheres and ask them to find their volumes.

1. a. If a cone, a cylinder, and a sphere all have the same radius and height, the volume of the cone is one-third the volume of the cylinder. The volume of the sphere is two-thirds the volume of the cylinder. The volume of the cone is one-half the volume of the sphere. For example, suppose they all have a height of 10 cm and a radius of 5 cm: The cylinder's volume is $25\pi \times 10 =$ about

785 cm^3. The cone's volume is one-third of 785 cm^3, or about 262 cm^3. The sphere's volume is two-thirds of 785 cm^3 or about 523 cm^3.

   b. You can think of a cylinder with the same radius as the sphere and a height of twice the radius. Because the sphere's volume will be two-thirds the cylinder's volume, you can find the volume of the sphere by finding the volume of the cylinder first. Multiply the area of the base of the cylinder (πr^2) by its height ($2r$), and then multiply by $\frac{2}{3}$ to find the volume of the sphere.

   c. You can think of a cylinder with the same radius and height as the cone. The cone will have one-third the volume of the cylinder, so the volume of the cone is $\frac{1}{3}\pi r^2 h$. Or, because $h = 2r$, the volume of the cone is $\frac{2}{3}\pi r^3$.

2. a. The volume of a pyramid is $\frac{1}{3}$ the volume of the prism.

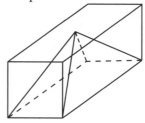

   b. Find the area of the base by multiplying the dimensions of the base. Multiply the area of the base by the height and take $\frac{1}{3}$ of the result. $V_{\text{pyramid}} = \frac{1}{3}$ area of base × height.

3. a. They both have volume equal to $\frac{1}{3}$ area of base × height of a cylinder or prism.

   b. They both have volume equal to area of base × height.

Investigation 5 · Scaling Boxes

Mathematical and Problem-Solving Goals

- Understand how changes in one or more dimensions of a rectangular prism affects the prism's volume
- Design rectangular prisms with a given volume
- Extend students' understanding of similarity to three-dimensional figures
- Understand the effect on surface area of applying a scale factor to a rectangular prism
- Understand the effect on volume of applying a scale factor to a rectangular prism
- Apply students' understanding of scale factor and its relationship to changes in 1-, 2-, and 3-dimensional measures

Summary of Problems

Problem 5.1 Building a Bigger Box

Students consider how to double the volume of a rectangular prism and examine how other measures change as a result.

Problem 5.2 Scaling Up the Compost Box

Students study the effects of applying scale factors to the dimensions of rectangular prisms to create similar prisms.

Problem 5.3 Building Model Ships

Students apply their knowledge of similarity and scale factors to explore the relationships between a model of a ship and the actual ship.

	Suggested Pacing	Materials for Students	Materials for Teachers	ACE Assignments
All	4 days			
5.1	1 day	Grid paper; scissors; tape	Article clip on next page	1–4, 20–26, 35
5.2	$1\frac{1}{2}$ days	Labsheet 5.2 (one per student); Boxes from 5.1 (optional)	Transparency 5.2; 1-2-3 and 2-4-6 boxes	5–17, 27, 36, 37
5.3	1 day			18, 19, 28–34, 38–40
MR	$\frac{1}{2}$ day			

Goals

- Understand how changes in one or more dimensions of a rectangular prism affect the prism's volume

- Design rectangular prisms with a given volume

In this problem, students investigate the effect that doubling the volume of a compost box has on other measures of the box.

The recipe for the 1-2-3 compost box is taken from the experience of a group of young campers at the Woldumar Nature Center in Lansing, Michigan. During summer day camp, the campers composted their lunch remains each day in a compost box. It is fairly easy to create a compost box.

Launch 5.1

To introduce the topic, read the following article to the class.

State worms to receive leftovers

Some Massachusetts state employees soon will have some slimy colleagues who work for table scraps.

The Conservation Law Foundation, an environmental group, is donating about a kilogram of red worms that will be relegated to office-building basements. Their mission will be to eat leftover food that usually is thrown away. It's a dirty job but the worms don't mind doing it.

Three green plastic bins went to the Executive Office of Environmental Affairs. Inside each were some shredded newspapers and 600 to 5,000 worms, depending on their age and size.

"It does work and it saves us money," said Doug Foy, foundation executive director.

*Reprinted with permission
from Associated Press.*

Tell the story of Deshondra's compost box. You might ask students to express their initial reactions to the questions. Students are likely to think that each dimension needs to be doubled. Collect other suggestions.

Distribute grid paper, scissors, and tape. Have each pair of students make models of a 1-2-3 box and the box that they think will decompose 1 pound of garbage. Students can work in pairs.

Explore 5.1

To make their models, students can either cut nets from grid paper or cut out rectangles and tape them together. All students should work with the same size unit. This will be easier to compare the effects of change in the summary of this problem and in Problem 5.2.

As students work on their models, ask them to explain why they think their new box will work.

Summarize 5.1

Students will have made different boxes that can decompose 1 pound of garbage per day.

A common box is 2-4-6. This box has a volume of 24 cubic units, or 8 times the volume of the 1-2-3 box. It will decompose 8 times as much garbage or 4 pounds of garbage in one day.

- *What is the volume of a 2-4-6 box?* (48 units^3)

- *Why, if we doubled the dimensions of the original box, is the volume not also doubled?*

Students may need to think hard about this question. You may want to stack 8 of the 1-2-3 boxes inside one 2-4-6 box.

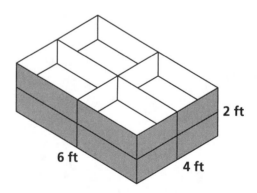

Some students may have done some calculations and found that to double the volume of the 1-2-3 box, you need to double one of its dimensions.

Some students will have a 2-2-3 box, a 1-4-3 box, or a 1-2-6 box. Be sure that students check that each of these boxes has the same volume and that this volume is twice the volume of a 1-2-3 box.

Other students may have just doubled the volume of the 1-2-3 box and then found a box that has a volume of 12 units^3. For example, a 1-1-12, or a 2-2-3 box will work. There are infinitely many boxes that will work if we allow fractional dimensions.

Suggested Questions Help students compare the various boxes.

- *Of the boxes (with volume 12 units^3) made by the people in our class, which will require the least material to make? Which will require the most material?*

Because the boxes are open, this calculation is trickier than we might expect. The previous observation about surface area being smaller for boxes closer to a cube does not tell the whole story. For instance, the two boxes on the top below are equally close to being cubes, but do not have the same surface area (40 units^2 and 46 units^2, respectively). Yet the box on the bottom has less surface area (28 units^2) than the second one, yet is not very cube-like:

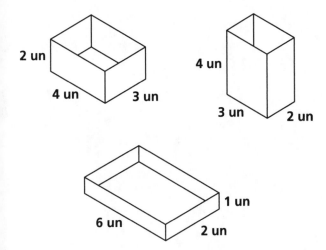

- *Which model would be the most practical if we wanted to make a real box for our classroom? Which would be the least practical?*

As a launch into the next problem, you could ask the class:

- *Look at all the boxes that were made. Which of the boxes are similar to each other?*

Some should be able to state that the 1-2-3 and 2-4-6 boxes look similar. Some students may even refer back to *Stretching and Shrinking* and talk about scale factor.

Save the boxes for demonstration in Problem 5.2, which explores similar rectangular prisms.

Going Further As an extra challenge, you could have some students search for the scale factor that would produce a box similar to the 1-2-3 box with twice its volume. This scale factor is the cube root of 2 (approx. 1.26). Students will likely not have experience with cube roots, but they can make a close estimate by trying several scale factors.

5.1 Building a Bigger Box

PACING 1 day

Mathematical Goals

- Understand how changes in one or more dimensions of a rectangular prism affect the prism's volume
- Design rectangular prisms with a given volume

Launch

Tell the story of Deshondra's compost box. You might ask students to express their initial reactions to the questions. Students are likely to think that each dimension needs to be doubled. Collect other suggestions.

Students can work in pairs.

Explore

Distribute grid paper, scissors, and tape. Have each pair of students make models of a 1-2-3 box and the box that they think will decompose 1 pound of garbage.

To make their models, students can either cut nets from grid paper or cut out rectangles and tape them together. All students should work with the same size unit. This will be easier to compare the effects of change in the summary of this problem and Problem 5.2.

As students work on their models, ask them to explain why they think their new box will work.

Materials
- Grid paper
- Scissors
- Tape

Summarize

Students will have made different boxes. A common box is 2-4-6. This box has a volume of 24 cubic units, 8 times the volume of the 1-2-3 box. It will decompose 8 times as much garbage or 4 pounds of garbage in one day.

- *What is the volume of a 2-4-6 box? Why, if we doubled the dimensions of the original box, is the volume not also doubled?*

Students may need to think hard about this question. You may want to stack 8 of the 1-2-3 boxes inside one 2-4-6 box.

Help students compare the various boxes.

- *Of the boxes made (with a volume of 12 units^3) by the people in our class, which will require the least material to make? Which will require the most material?*

- *Which model would be the most practical if we wanted to make a real box for our classroom? Which would be the least practical?*

As a launch into the next problem, you could ask the class:

- *Which of all the boxes made are similar to each other?*

Save the boxes for demonstration in Problem 5.2, which explores similar rectangular prisms.

Materials
- Student notebooks

ACE Assignment Guide for Problem 5.1

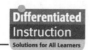

Core 2–4, 24, 26
Other *Applications* 1; *Connections* 20–23, 25, 35

Adapted For suggestions about adapting ACE exercises, see the CMP *Special Needs Handbook*.
Connecting to Prior Units 20–23: *Covering and Surrounding*; 24: *Stretching and Shrinking*

Answers to Problem 5.1

A. The 1-2-3 box has a volume of 6 ft³. Models will vary but the new box should have a volume of 12 ft³. Sample boxes: 1-by-2-by-6; 2-by-2-by-3; and 1-by-4-by-3.

Note that because the boxes are open, a 1-by-2-by-6 box (for example) would require different amounts of materials depending on which dimension is the height.

B. 1. Answers for the dimensions will vary, but the box should have a volume of 12 ft³. Typically, students will double one of the dimensions.

   2. Two of the original boxes will fit in the new one.

   3. The volume of the new box is twice the original one.

C. Answers will vary depending on the placement of the dimensions and which dimensions form the base and the open top. Some samples:

Length (ft)	Width (ft)	Height (ft)	Surface Area (sq. ft)
2	2	3	28
3	4	1	26
2	6	1	28

Scaling Up the Compost Box

Goals

- Understand the effect on surface area of applying a scale factor to a rectangular prism

- Understand the effect on volume of applying a scale factor to a rectangular prism

- Extend students' understanding of similarity to three-dimensional figures

In this problem, students generalize the findings from Problem 5.1 and look at what happens when the dimensions of a 1-2-3 box are multiplied by various scale factors. If the same number multiplies each dimension, the resulting box is similar to a 1-2-3 box.

A Pro-Worm Testimonial

A teacher from Oregon wrote the following: "Ever since I heard about worm boxes, I had planned on starting one. This activity offered a great excuse. I had a book on composting that suggested a ratio of 2.5 pounds of paper per cubic foot of space and 3 pounds of water for every pound of paper. My box was 20 inches by 24 inches by 12 inches, so I started doing my math to figure out what I had to do to set this thing up. What a great activity for the kids. I went into class with a scale, newspaper, soil, two gallons of water, a mixing bin, some garbage from my kitchen and, of course, the worm box and worms. I was wearing a pin that said, 'Worms eat my garbage.' Kids noticed. They were excited. My pet worms are now happily digesting garbage under my table at school."

Launch 5.2

Suggested Questions Hold up the 1-2-3 and 2-4-6 boxes. Ask:

- *Are these two boxes mathematically similar?* (various answers)

- *How can we check?* (Measure and compare corresponding sides. Look for a common scale factor.)

- *What is the relationship between the corresponding dimensions of the two boxes?* (The larger box's dimensions are twice those of the smaller box.)

- *What is the relationship between the surface areas of the two boxes?* (The surface area of the larger box is 4 times that of the smaller box.)

- *What is the relationship between the volumes of the two boxes?* (The volume of the larger box is 8 times the volume of the smaller box.)

- *What is the scale factor from the 1-2-3 to the 2-4-6 box?* (The scale factor is 2.)

- *So, are these two boxes similar?* (These two boxes are similar because each dimension is multiplied by the same factor: 2.)

Demonstrate the volume relationship by stacking eight 1-2-3 boxes inside the 2-4-6 box.

Tell the class that Ms. Fernandez's class is building a variety of similar compost boxes. Remind students that the compost boxes are open on top.

- *What is the surface area of a 1-2-3 box?* (16 square feet)

- *What is the volume of a 1-2-3 box?* (6 cubic feet)

- *What feature of the box does the amount of garbage that is decomposed each day relate to?* (volume)

- *If we double the amount of garbage, what feature of the 1-2-3 box will we need to double?* (volume)

- *If we double the dimensions of the 1-2-3 box, will we also double the garbage it can decompose?* (No, we will increase the amount of garbage it can decompose—a function of the volume—by a factor of 8, not 2.)

Ask the class what they think will happen to the volume and surface area of a 1-2-3 box if its dimensions are tripled or quadrupled.

- *If you tripled each dimension of a 1-2-3 box, what would happen to the surface area?* (It would be 9 times the original, or 3^2.)

- *How do you know?*

- *If you tripled each dimension of a 1-2-3 box, what would happen to the volume?* (It would be 27 times the original, or 3^3.)

- *How do you know?*

- *How much plywood would be needed to make the new box?* (144 ft^2)

- *How many pounds of garbage could the new box decompose?* (27 times 0.5, or 13.5 lb; the amount of garbage is similar to the volume.)

Let the class offer a few conjectures. Tell them that these types of questions are what they will be exploring in this problem.

Let the class work in groups of 3 to 4.

Explore 5.2

The students in each group should work together to find the volumes and surface areas of all the boxes that the group designs. If students are struggling with this problem, you may need to review the properties of similar rectangles. The idea of similar rectangular prisms should follow naturally.

Summarize 5.2

Put up the chart.

Suggested Questions Help the class summarize what they have found. Ask:

- *What happens to the volume of a box if its dimensions are tripled?* (The volume will be 27 times as great. It would take 27 of the original boxes to fill the new box.)

- *What happens to the volume if the dimensions are quadrupled?* (The volume will be 64 times as great. It would take 64 of the original boxes to fill the new box.)

- *What happens to the surface area of a box if its dimensions are tripled?* (The surface area will be 9 times as great.)

- *What happens to the surface area if the dimensions are quadrupled?* (The surface area will be 16 times as great.)

Ask questions to assess how well students are grasping the ideas of similarity and scale factor as applied to three-dimensional figures.

- *What are the dimensions, surface area, and volume of a box similar to a 1-2-3 box if the scale factor is 9?* (The dimensions are 9 feet by 18 feet by 27 feet. The surface area is $16 \times 81 = 1{,}296$ square feet, and the volume is $6 \times 729 = 4{,}374$ cubic feet.)

- *What are the dimensions of a box that is similar to a 1-2-3 box but has a surface area of 1600 square feet? What is the scale factor from the 1-2-3 box to the new box?* (The surface area of a 1-2-3 box is 16 square feet, so the scale factor from the small box to the large box is 10. This means that the new box's dimensions are 10 feet by 20 feet by 30 feet.)

- *What are the dimensions of a box that is similar to a 1-2-3 box but has a volume of 10,368 cubic feet? What is the scale factor from the 1-2-3 box to the new box?* (The scale factor is $10{,}368 \div 6 = 1{,}728$. We need to find a number whose cube is 1,728. We know that 103 is 1,000, so it must be greater than 10 but not much. 113 is 1,331, and 123 is 1,728, so the scale factor is 12. The new box's dimensions are 12 feet by 24 feet by 36 feet.)

- *If the scale factor from a 1-2-3 box to a larger box is 4, how many 1-2-3 boxes will fit in the large box?* (The new box will hold $4 \times 4 \times 4 = 64$ of the 1-2-3 boxes.)

- *Which measurement is the change in garbage associated with?* (volume)

5.2 Scaling Up the Compost Box

Mathematical Goals

- Extend students' understanding of similarity to three-dimensional figures

- Understand the effect on surface area of applying a scale factor to a rectangular prism

- Understand the effect on volume of applying a scale factor to a rectangular prism

Launch

Hold up the 1-2-3 and 2-4-6 boxes.

- *Are these two boxes mathematically similar?*

- *How can we check?*

- *What is the relationship between the corresponding dimensions of the two boxes?*

- *What is the relationship between the surface areas of the two boxes?*

- *What is the relationship between the volumes of the two boxes?*

- *What is the scale factor from the 1-2-3 to the 2-4-6 box? So, are these two boxes similar?*

Demonstrate the volume relationship by stacking eight 1-2-3 boxes inside the 2-4-6 box. Tell the class that Ms. Fernandez's class is building a variety of similar compost boxes. Remind students that the compost boxes are open on top.

- *What feature of the box does the amount of garbage that is decomposed each day relate to?*

- *If we double the amount of garbage, what feature of the 1-2-3 box will we need to double?*

Ask the class what they think will happen to the volume and surface area of a 1-2-3 box if its dimensions are tripled or quadrupled.

Let the class offer a few conjectures. Tell them that these types of questions are what they will be exploring in this problem.

Have students work in groups of 3 or 4.

Materials

- Transparency 5.2
- Labsheet 5.2
- 1-2-3 and 2-4-6 boxes
- Boxes from Problem 5.1

Explore

The students in each group should work together to find the volumes and surface areas of all the boxes that the group designs. If students are struggling with this problem, you may need to further discuss the properties of similar rectangles. The idea of similar rectangular prisms should follow naturally.

Put up the chart. Help the class summarize what they have found.

- *What happens to the volume of a box if its dimensions are tripled?*
- *What happens to the volume if the dimensions are quadrupled?*
- *What happens to the surface area of a box if its dimensions are tripled?*
- *What happens to the surface area if the dimensions are quadrupled?*

Ask questions to assess how well students are grasping the ideas of similarity and scale factor as applied to three-dimensional figures.

Materials
- Student notebooks

ACE Assignment Guide for Problem 5.2

Differentiated Instruction
Solutions for All Learners

Core 8, 10–14
Other *Applications* 5–7, 9, 15–17; *Connections* 27; *Extensions* 36, 37; unassigned choices from previous problems

Adapted For suggestions about adapting Exercise 17 and other ACE exercises, see the CMP *Special Needs Handbook*.

Answers to Problem 5.2

A. (Figure 1)

B. Once the surface area of the 1-2-3 box is determined, the surface area of a similar box is *original surface area* × (*scale factor*)^2. For example, the surface area of the original 1-2-3 box is 16 ft^2. The surface area of the 2-4-6 box, which has been increased by a scale factor of 2, is 64 ft^2 or 16 × 2^2. The surface area of the 3-6-9 box, where 3 is the scale factor, is 144 ft^2, or 16 × 3^2. Having a closed compost box will not change the factor.

C. Once the volume of the original 1-2-3 box is determined, the volume of a similar box is *original volume* × (*scale factor*)^3. For example, the volume of the original 1-2-3 box is 6 ft^3. The volume of the 2-4-6 box, which has been increased by a scale factor of 2, is 48 ft^3 or 6 × 2^3. The volume of the 3-6-9 box, where the scale factor is 3, is 162 ft^3 or 6 × 3^3.

D. The amount of garbage that can be decomposed in a day is related to the volume of the box. Thus, once the amount of decomposed garbage for the original 1-2-3 box is determined, the amount for a similar box is the original amount × (scale factor)^3. The amount of decomposed garbage in the original 1-2-3 box is $\frac{1}{2}$ pound of garbage per day. The amount of garbage decomposed in the 2-4-6 box, which has been increased by a scale factor of 2, is 4 lbs. or $\frac{1}{2}$ × 2^3.

E. If the scale factor between the 1-2-3 box and a similar box is N, for the similar box, the new dimensions are: N-2N-3N, its surface area is N^2 times the surface area of the 1-2-3 box, and its volume is N^3 times the volume of the 1-2-3 box.

Figure 1

Compost Box Project

Open Box (h-w-l)	Scale Factor	Surface Area (sq. ft)	Volume (cu. ft)	Amount of Garbage Decomposed in a Day (lb)	Number of Worms Needed
1-2-3	1	16	6	0.5	1,000
2-4-6	2	64	48	4	8,000
3-6-9	3	144	162	13.5	27,000
4-8-12	4	256	384	32	64,000
8-16-24	8	1,024	3,072	256	512,000
10-20-30	10	1,600	6,000	500	1,000,000

Building Model Ships

Goal

- Apply students' understanding of scale factor and its relationship to changes in 1-, 2-, and 3-dimensional measures

Launch 5.3

Ask the class if any of them have made models of ships or other objects. Many students may not have made models but have bought models of airplanes, cars, houses, and so on.

- *How does a model compare to the object it is a model of?* (Usually, it is smaller but similar in shape to the original.)

Pose the problem that Natasha has of trying to visualize the actual ship from the model.
Students can work on the problem in pairs.

Explore 5.3

Suggested Questions Ask students how they found their answers.

- *Did you use the scale factor? In what way?*
- *Compare this situation to the worm boxes.*

Summarize 5.3

Go over the questions. Ask students to explain how the scale factor is used.

Suggested Questions Other questions that can be asked:

- *If it takes 0.1 gallon of paint to paint the floor of the model, how many gallons will it take to paint the floor of the actual ship?* (4,000 gallons. This is related to area.)

- *What are some other measures on the ship that would be 200 times as large?* (anything relating to lengths: heights of doors, length of the swimming pool on the poop deck, length of the anchor chain, etc.)

- *What are some measures on the ship that would be 40,000 times as large as on the model?* (anything having to do with areas: area of the sheets on the beds, surface of the water in the pool, area of the portrait of the ship's captain, etc.)

- *What are some measures on the ship that would be 8,000,000 times as large as on the model?* (anything having to do with volumes: amount of water in the pool, etc.)

- *What are some measures on a ship that would not change?* (the number of corridors, the number of flag poles, etc.)

Check for Understanding

Bring in a model car or dollhouse. Give some dimensions of either the model or the real thing. Ask questions about it. Or, ask the class to make up questions that could be asked about the model and the real thing.

5.3 Building Model Ships

Mathematical Goal

- Apply students' understanding of scale factor and its relationship to changes in 1-, 2-, and 3-dimensional measures

Launch

Ask the class if any of them have made models of ships or other objects. Many students may not have made models but have bought models of airplanes, cars, houses, and so on.

- *How does a model compare to the object it is a model of?*

Pose the problem that Natasha has of trying to visualize the actual ship from the model.

Students can work on the problem in pairs.

Explore

Ask students how they found their answers.

- *Did they use the scale factor? In what way?*

Summarize

Go over the questions. Ask students to explain how the scale factor is used.

Other questions that can be asked:

- *If it takes 0.1 gallon of paint to paint the floor of the model, how many gallons will it take to paint the floor of the actual ship?*
- *What are some other measures on the ship that would be 200 times as large?*
- *What are some measures on the ship that would be 40,000 times as large as on the model?*
- *What are some measures on the ship that would be 8,000,000 times as large as on the model?*

Materials
- Student notebooks

ACE Assignment Guide for Problem 5.3

Core 18, 19
Other *Connections* 28–34; *Extensions* 38–40; unassigned choices from previous problems

Adapted For suggestions about adapting ACE exercises, see the CMP *Special Needs Handbook*.
Connecting to Prior Units 28: *Stretching and Shrinking*; 29: *Covering and Surrounding*; 33: *Bits and Pieces II*; 34: *Bits and Pieces III*

Answers to Problem 5.3

A. **1.** $25 \times 200 = 5{,}000$ cm or 50 m

   2. 15 cm ($3{,}000/200 = 15$)

B. $20 \times 200^2 = 800{,}000$ cm^2 or 80 m^2

C. **1.** Height $= 4 \times 200 = 800$ cm or 8 m, radius $= 1.5 \times 200 = 300$ cm or 3 m

   2. About 226 m^3

   3. About 151 m^2 (Note: The top and bottom of the smokestack are open.)

The student edition pages for this investigation begin on the next page.

Scaling Boxes

The cost of packaging materials and finding enough landfill for garbage and waste materials is becoming a problem for many communities. Some communities are looking at composting as a way to recycle garbage into productive soil.

Composting is a method for turning organic waste into rich soil. Today, many people have compost boxes that break down kitchen waste quickly and with little odor. The secret is in the worms!

62   Filling and Wrapping

Notes _____

_____

_____

_____

Recipe for a 1-2-3 Compost Box

- Start with an open rectangular wood box that is 1 foot high, 2 feet wide, and 3 feet long. This is a 1-2-3 box.

- Mix 10 pounds of shredded newspaper with 15 quarts of water. Put the mixture in the 1-2-3 box.

- Add a few handfuls of soil.

- Add about 1,000 redworms (about 1 pound).

Every day, mix collected kitchen waste with the soil in the box. The worms will do the rest of the work, turning the waste into new soil. A 1-2-3 box will decompose about 0.5 pound of garbage each day.

5.1 Building a Bigger Box

Deshondra chose composting as the topic of her science project. She plans to build a compost box at home and to keep records of the amount of soil produced over several weeks. She estimates that her family throws away 1 pound of garbage a day.

Problem 5.1 Doubling the Volume of a Rectangular Prism

Deshondra wants to build a box that will decompose twice the amount of the 1-2-3 box.

A. Using grid paper, make scale models of a 1-2-3 box that will decompose 0.5 pound of garbage per day and a box that will decompose 1 pound of garbage per day.

B. 1. What are the dimensions of the new box?

   2. How many of the original boxes will fit into the new box?

   3. How is the volume of the new box related to the volume of the original box?

C. How much plywood is needed to construct an open 1-pound box?

ACE Homework starts on page 67.

Investigation 5 Scaling Boxes   **63**

Notes _____

_____

_____

_____

5.2 Scaling Up the Compost Box

In *Stretching and Shrinking,* you studied similar two-dimensional figures. The ideas you learned also apply to three-dimensional figures. For example, two rectangular prisms are similar if the ratios of the lengths of corresponding edges are equal. A 2-4-6 box is similar to the 1-2-3 box.

The *scale factor* is the number that each dimension of one rectangular prism must be multiplied by to get the dimensions of a similar prism. The scale factor from the 1-2-3 box to the 2-4-6 box is 2 because each edge length of the 1-2-3 box must be multiplied by 2 to get the corresponding edge length of the 2-4-6 box.

Problem 5.2 Applying Scale Factors to Rectangular Prisms

Ms. Fernandez's class decides that building and maintaining a compost is a fascinating project. One student suggests that they could earn money selling worms and soil to a local nursery.

They decide to build different-sized boxes that are similar to the 1-2-3 box. They need to know how much material is needed to build the boxes and how much garbage each box will decompose in a day.

A. Copy and complete the table.

Compost Box Project

Open Box (h-w-ℓ)	Scale Factor	Surface Area (ft²)	Volume (ft³)	Amount of Garbage Decomposed in a Day	Number of Worms Needed
1-2-3	■	■	■	■	■
2-4-6	■	■	■	■	■
3-6-9	■	■	■	■	■
4-8-12	■	■	■	■	■
■	■	■	■	■	■
■	■	1,024	■	■	■
■	■	■	■	■	■
■	■	■	6,000	■	■

64 Filling and Wrapping

STUDENT PAGE

Notes _____

_____

_____

_____

STUDENT PAGE

B. How is the change in surface area from a 1-2-3 box to a similar box related to the scale factor from the 1-2-3 box to the similar box? Suppose the compost box has a top. Will your answer change? Explain.

C. How is the change in volume from a 1-2-3 box to a similar box related to the scale factor from the 1-2-3 box to the similar box? Explain.

D. How is the change in decomposed garbage related to the scale factor? Explain.

E. Suppose the scale factor between the 1-2-3 box and a similar box is N. Describe the dimensions, surface area, and volume of the similar box.

ACE Homework starts on page 67.

ACE Homework starts on page 67.

5.3 Building Model Ships

Builders and architects often make models of cars, ships, buildings, and parks. A model is useful in determining several aspects of the building process, including structural strength, expense, and appearance.

Notes _____

_____

_____

_____

Natasha builds a model ship from a kit. She tries to picture what the actual ship looks like. The scale factor from the model to the actual ship is 200.

A. 1. If the length of the model is 25 centimeters, what is the length of the actual ship?

   2. If the length of the flagpole on the actual ship is 30 meters, what is the length of the flagpole on the model?

B. The area of a rectangular floor on the model is 20 square centimeters. What is the area of the floor on the actual ship?

C. The cylindrical smoke stack on the model has a height of 4 centimeters and a radius of 1.5 centimeters.

   1. What are the dimensions of the smoke stack on the actual ship?

   2. What is the volume of the smoke stack on the actual ship?

   3. What is the surface area of the smoke stack on the actual ship?

ACE Homework starts on page 67.

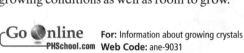

Did You Know?

Most minerals occur naturally as crystals. Every crystal has an orderly, internal pattern of atoms, with a distinctive way of locking new atoms into that pattern. As the pattern repeats, larger similar-shaped crystals are formed. The shape of the resulting crystal, such as a cube (like salt) or a six-sided form (like a snowflake), is a similar crystal.

As crystals grow, differences in temperature and chemical composition cause fascinating variations. But you will rarely find in your backyard the perfectly shaped mineral crystals that you see in a museum. In order to readily show their geometric form and flat surfaces, crystals need ideal or controlled growing conditions as well as room to grow.

Go Online
PHSchool.com
For: Information about growing crystals
Web Code: ane-9031

66 Filling and Wrapping

Notes _____

_____

_____

_____

Applications

1. **a.** Make a sketch of an open 1-3-5 box. Label the edges of the box.

   b. Sketch three boxes that have twice the volume of a 1-3-5 box. Label each box with its dimensions.

   c. Are any of the three boxes in part (b) similar to the 1-3-5 box? Explain.

For Exercises 2–4, find the volume and the surface area of each closed box.

2. 1-2-2   3. 1.5-1.5-3   4. 2-4-1

For Exercises 5–7, decide if each pair of cylinders are similar. For each pair of similar cylinders, describe how many times larger one is than the other.

5. Cylinder 1: height = 10 centimeters, radius = 5 centimeters
   Cylinder 2: height = 5 centimeters, radius = 2.5 centimeters

6. Cylinder 1: height = 10 centimeters, radius = 5 centimeters
   Cylinder 2: height = 30 centimeters, radius = 15 centimeters

7. Cylinder 1: height = 10 centimeters, radius = 5 centimeters
   Cylinder 2: height = 15 centimeters, radius = 10 centimeters

8. **a.** Make a sketch of an open 2-2-3 box and an open 2-2-6 box. Label the edges of the boxes.

   b. Find the volume of each box in part (a).

   c. Find the surface area of each box in part (a).

   d. Suppose you want to adapt the 1-2-3 compost box recipe for the boxes in part (a). How many worms and how much paper and water would you need for each box?

9. **a.** Give the dimensions of a rectangular box that will decompose 5 pounds of garbage per day. Explain your reasoning.

   b. Is your box similar to the 1-2-3 box? Explain.

Investigation 5 Scaling Boxes   **67**

Notes _____

_____

_____

_____

10. One cube has edges measuring 1 foot. A second cube has edges measuring 2 feet. A third cube has edges measuring 3 feet.

   a. Make scale drawings of the three cubes. For each cube, tell what length in the drawing represents 1 foot.

   b. Find the surface area of each cube.

   c. Describe what happens to the surface area of a cube when the edge lengths are doubled, tripled, quadrupled, and so on.

11. a. Find the volume of each cube in Exercise 10.

   b. Describe what happens to the volume of a cube when the edge lengths are doubled, tripled, quadrupled, and so on.

For Exercises 12–14, decide if each pair of rectangular boxes is similar. For each pair of similar boxes, describe how many times larger one box is than the other box.

Homework Help Online
PHSchool.com

For: Help with
Exercises 12–14
Web Code: ane-6512

12. 1-2-5 and 3-6-15

13. 2-3-2 and 5-6-5

14. 2-1-4 and 3-1.5-6

15. In the United States, an average of 2.7 pounds of garbage per person is delivered to landfills each day. A cubic foot of compressed garbage weighs about 50 pounds.

   a. Estimate the amount of garbage produced by a family of four in one year.

   b. Estimate the amount of garbage produced by the families of a class of 20 students in one year. Assume each family has four people.

16. Each year the United States generates 450 million cubic yards of solid waste. Mr. Costello's classroom is 42 feet long, 30 feet wide, and 12 feet high. How many rooms of this size would be needed to hold all this garbage?

68   Filling and Wrapping

STUDENT PAGE

Notes _____

_____

_____

_____

17. For every ton of paper that is recycled, about 17 trees and 3.3 cubic yards of landfill space are saved. In the United States, the equivalent of 500,000 trees are used each week to produce the Sunday papers. Suppose all the Sunday papers this week are made from recycled paper. How much landfill is saved?

In Exercises 18 and 19, a company that specializes in creating models of buildings is hired to develop models of pools for the upcoming summer Olympics. The pools are rectangular prisms. The scale factor from the model to the actual pool is 120.

18. a. The dimensions of the actual diving pool are 20 meters by 20 meters by 4.9 meters. What are the dimensions of the model diving pool?

b. What is the capacity (volume) of the actual diving pool. What is the capacity of the model diving pool?

c. What is the surface area of the actual diving pool? What is the surface area of the model diving pool? (Do not include the surface of the water.)

19. a. The planned water capacity of the pool used for water polo and swimming is 1,650 cubic meters. What is the capacity of the model pool?

b. A sunken corridor with viewing windows is planned for the diving pool. The area of a window in the actual setting is 160 square feet. What is the area of the window on the model?

Investigation 5 Scaling Boxes   **69**

Notes _____

_____

_____

_____

Connections

20. For parts (a)–(e), find the measure that makes a true statement.

Go Online
PHSchool.com
For: Multiple-Choice Skills Practice
Web Code: ana-6554

   a. 1 square foot = ■ square inches

   b. 1 square yard = ■ square inches

   c. 1 cubic yard = ■ cubic feet

   d. 2 square yards = ■ square inches

   e. 3 square yards = ■ square inches

   f. For parts (a), (b), and (e) above, draw a diagram to justify your answer.

For Exercises 21–23, find the measure that makes a true statement.

21. 4 square meters = ■ square centimeters

22. 1 cubic meter = ■ cubic centimeters

23. 6 cubic centimeters = ■ cubic millimeters

24. For the compost boxes in Problem 5.1, find the ratios in parts (a)–(c).

   a. the length of each side of the 1-2-3 box to the length of the corresponding side of the 2-4-6 box

   b. the surface area of the 1-2-3 box to the surface area of the 2-4-6 box

   c. the volume of the 1-2-3 box to the volume of the 2-4-6 box

   d. How is each ratio in parts (a)–(c) related to the scale factor from the 1-2-3 box to the 2-4-6 box?

25. At the movie theater, a large cylindrical container of popcorn costs $5.00, and a small cylindrical container costs $2.50. Denzel thinks that the heights of the containers are about the same and that the radius of the large container is about twice the radius of the small container. To get the most popcorn for his $5.00, should Denzel buy one large popcorn or two small popcorns? Explain.

$2.50 $2.50 $5.00

70   Filling and Wrapping

Notes _____

_____

_____

_____

26. A compost company builds and sells 1-2-3 compost boxes. They need to store a supply of the boxes in their warehouse to fill customers' orders. The sketches below show a 1-2-3 box on the right and the space in the warehouse allotted for the boxes on the left.

Not drawn to scale

  a. How many 1-2-3 boxes can be stored in one layer on the floor of the storage space?

  b. How many layers of boxes can be stacked in the storage space?

  c. How many boxes can be stored in the storage space?

27. Mary's class decides to build a cylindrical compost box. Mary calculates that a cylindrical container with a height of 2 feet and a radius of 1 foot would decompose 0.5 pound of garbage each day. She calls this container a 1-2 cylinder.

  a. How does the volume of the 1-2 cylinder compare with the volume of the 1-2-3 box?

  b. How does the surface area of the 1-2 cylinder compare with the surface area of the 1-2-3 box?

  c. Mary's class estimates that they throw away about 1 pound of garbage at school each day. What size cylinder should they build to handle this much garbage?

28. The two legs of a right triangle are in the ratio 3 : 4.

  a. Sketch and label the described triangle. Then sketch and label two other similar right triangles.

  b. Suppose you create a similar right triangle by doubling the length of the legs. How will the area of the first triangle be related to the area of the second triangle?

Investigation 5 Scaling Boxes   **71**

Notes _____

_____

_____

_____

29. A football field is 120 yards long, including the end zones, and $53\frac{1}{3}$ yards wide.

   a. How many square yards are in the football field?

   b. How many square feet are in the football field?

   c. What is the relationship between the number of square yards and square feet in the football field?

   d. Describe what happens to the number of square feet in the area of a rectangle when the unit of measure for length and width is $\frac{1}{3}$ the size of the original unit.

For Exercises 30–32, find the volume and surface area of each box shown.

30.

31.

32.

33. After a container of water is poured into a cylindrical tank, the tank is $\frac{2}{9}$ full. How many containers of water are needed to fill the tank to $\frac{3}{4}$ full?

$\frac{2}{9}$ full

STUDENT PAGE

Notes _____

_____

_____

_____

34. Anna uses exactly one small can of red paint to cover a strip around the top of an open chest. The red strip around the top is 0.15 of the total surface area (without the top and bottom of the chest).

   a. How many small cans of blue paint does she need to paint the rest?

   b. What is the surface area of the chest, not including the top and bottom?

Extensions

35. The following sketches show the front, top, and right side views of a "tilted box" in which two of the six faces are non-rectangular parallelograms. The top and the bottom faces are identical rectangles, and the right and left faces are identical rectangles. (This is called an *oblique prism*.)

      Front   **Top**   **Right**

   a. Make a sketch of the box.

   b. What measurements do you need to find the volume of the box? How can you use these measurements to find the volume?

   c. What measurements do you need to find the surface area of the box? How can you use these measurements to find the surface area?

36. Is the price of a box of cereal directly related to its volume? Collect some data to help you answer this question.

   a. Record the dimensions and prices of two or three different-sized boxes of the same cereal brand.

   b. Calculate the volume of each box.

   c. Calculate the cost per unit of volume for each box. Compare the results for the different boxes.

   d. Write a short report summarizing what you learned about the relationship between box size and cereal price.

37. A cake, a loaf of bread, or a brick of cheese could be called a "sliceable" rectangular prism.

   a. How many different ways can you slice such a prism into two pieces of equal volume?

   b. If the prism were a cube, how many ways could you slice it into two pieces of equal volume?

For each pair of cylinders in Exercises 38–40, find the ratio of each measurement of Cylinder A to the corresponding measurement of Cylinder B.

   a. the radius   **b.** the height

   c. the surface area   **d.** the volume

38. The dimensions of Cylinder A are twice the dimensions of Cylinder B.

39. The dimensions of Cylinder A are three times the dimensions of Cylinder B.

40. The dimensions of Cylinder A are four times the dimensions of Cylinder B.

Notes _____

_____

_____

_____

Mathematical Reflections 5

In this investigation, you learned how changing the dimensions of a rectangular box affects its volume and surface area. These questions will help you summarize what you have learned.

Think about your answers to these questions. Discuss your ideas with other students and your teacher. Then write a summary of your findings in your notebook.

1. Suppose you want to build a rectangular box with eight times the volume of a given rectangular box. How can you determine the possible dimensions for the new box? Are the two boxes similar? Explain.

2. Describe how the volume and surface area of a rectangular prism change as each of its dimensions is doubled, tripled, quadrupled, and so on.

Notes _____

_____

_____

_____

Investigation

ACE
Assignment Choices

Differentiated Instruction
Solutions for All Learners

Problem 5.1
Core 2–4, 24, 26
Other *Applications* 1; *Connections* 20–23, 25, 33; *Extension* 35

Problem 5.2
Core 8, 10–14
Other *Applications* 5–7, 9, 15–17; *Connections* 27, 33–34; *Extensions* 36–37; unassigned choices from previous problems

Problem 5.3
Core 18–19
Other *Connections* 28–34; *Extensions* 38–40; unassigned choices from previous problems

Adapted For suggestions about adapting Exercise 17 and other ACE exercises, see the CMP *Special Needs Handbook*.
Connecting to Prior Units 20–23, 29: *Covering and Surrounding*; 24, 28: *Stretching and Shrinking*; 33: *Bits and Pieces II*; 34: *Bits and Pieces III*

Applications

1. a.

b. Some possible sketches:

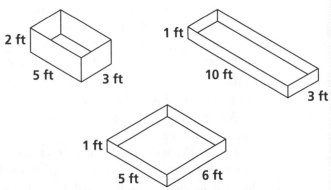

c. To make a box that is similar to a 1-3-5 box, you would need to scale each dimension of the box equally. It is possible to double the volume and create a similar box by using the cube root of 2 as the scale factor, but this is probably not a box that a student thought to use in Question B.

2. a. 4 ft^3 **b.** 16 ft^2

3. a. 6.75 ft^3 **b.** 22.5 ft^2

4. a. 8 ft^3 **b.** 28 ft^2

5. Similar. Because the height and radius of cylinder 1 are 2 times larger than those in cylinder 2, cylinder 1 is 8 ($2 \times 2 \times 2$) times larger than cylinder 2.

6. Similar. Because the height and radius of cylinder 2 are 3 times larger than those in cylinder 1, cylinder 2 is 27 ($3 \times 3 \times 3$) times larger than cylinder 1.

7. Not similar.

8. a. Students' boxes may have different orientations from the ones below:

b. 2-2-3 box: 12 ft^3; 2-2-6 box: 24 ft^3
c. 2-2-3 box: 26 ft^2; 2-2-6 box: 44 ft^2

d. 2-2-3 box: 2,000 worms, 20 pounds of paper, and 30 quarts of water

2-2-6 box: 4,000 worms, 40 pounds of paper, and 60 quarts of water

9. a. Answers will vary. If a 1-2-3 box that has a volume of 6 ft³ will decompose 0.5 pound of garbage per day, then a box that will decompose 5 pounds of garbage per day needs to have 10 times the volume or hold 60 ft³ of garbage. Possible dimensions for such a box are 5-6-2, 10-3-2, 4-5-3 and 12-5-1.

b. To make a box that would compost 5 pounds of garbage per day and be similar to the 1-2-3, box you would need to scale each dimension of the box equally. It is possible to increase the volume ten times to create a similar box by using the cube root of 10 as the scale factor, but this is probably not a box that a student thought to use in Question A.

10. a. Scales will vary; the scale used below is 4 mm = 1 ft.

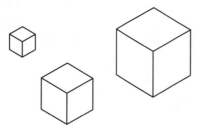

b. 1-ft cube: 6 ft²; 2-ft cube: 24 ft²; 3-ft cube: 54 ft²

c. When the dimensions are doubled, the new surface area is 4 times the original. When they are tripled, the new surface area is 9 times the original. When they are quadrupled, the new surface area is 16 times the original. In general, when the dimensions are increased *n* times, the new surface area is n^2 times the original.

11. a. 1-ft cube: 1 ft³; 2-ft cube: 8 ft³; 3-ft cube: 27 ft³

b. When the dimensions are doubled, the new volume is 8 times the original. When they are tripled, the new volume is 27 times the original. When they are quadrupled, the new volume is 64 times the original. In general, when the dimensions are increased *n* times, the new volume is n^3 times the original.

12. Similar. Because each dimension of 3-6-15 is 3 times larger than each of 1-2-5, the 3-6-15 box is 27 ($3 \times 3 \times 3$) times larger than the 1-2-5 box.

13. Not similar.

14. Similar. Since each dimension of 3-1.5-6 is 1.5 times larger than each of 2-1-4, the box 3-1.5-6 is 3.375 ($1.5 \times 1.5 \times 1.5$) times larger than the 2-1-4 box.

15. a. In a year, a family of four would produce $2.7 \times 4 \times 365 = 3,942$ pounds of garbage and use $3,942 \div 50 = 78.84$ ft³ of landfill.

b. Answers will vary. Over a year, the families of a class of 20 students would produce $20 \times 3,845 = 77,000$ pounds of garbage and use $77,000 \div 50 = 1,540$ ft³ of landfill.

16. This classroom will hold $42 \times 30 \times 12 = 15,120$ ft³ of garbage or $15,120 \div 3^3 = 560$ yd³. It would take $450,000,000 \div 560 \approx 803,571$ classrooms of the given size to hold the garbage.

17. If the Sunday papers were made from recycled paper, $500,000 \div 17 \approx 29,412$ tons of recycled paper would be required, and $29,412 \times 3.3 \approx 97,060$ yd³ of landfill would be saved.

(Note: If you have information about the amount of paper recycled in your community, this might make a good discussion. Students could keep track of the paper thrown out—or saved for recycling—in their house in one week.)

18. a. The dimensions of the model diving pool are approximately 0.17 m by 0.17 m by 0.04 m or $\frac{1}{6}$ m by $\frac{1}{6}$ m by $\frac{4}{100}$ m.

b. The capacity of the actual diving pool is 1960 m³ and the capacity of the model diving pool is approximately 0.001 m³.

c. The surface area of the actual diving pool is 792 m² and the surface area of the model diving pool is about 0.055m².

19. a. The capacity of the model competition pool is about 0.00095 m³.

b. The area of the model viewing window is approximately 0.01ft².

Connections

20. a. 144 in.^{2} **b.** 1,296 in.^{2}

    c. 27 ft^3 **d.** 2,592 in.^{2}

    e. 3,888 in.^{2}

    f. For Question A, students can draw a 12-by-12 grid, and for Question B, a 36-by-36 grid. For the diagram for Question E, students can show there are 1,296 in.^{2} in 1 yd^2 (the 36 inch-by-36 inch representation from Question B), then draw three of them to get 3,888 in.^{2}.

21. 40,000 cm^2

22. 1,000,000 cm^3

23. 6,000 mm^3

24. a. 1 to 2   **b.** 1 to 4   **c.** 1 to 8

    d. When the ratio of side length to side length is 1 : 2 or $\frac{1}{2}$, the surface area ratio is $(\frac{1}{2})^2$ and the volume ratio is $(\frac{1}{2})^3$.

25. The larger container is the better buy; for twice the money, the larger size contains four times the popcorn because doubling the radius of a cylinder quadruples its volume.

26. a. 100 boxes

    b. 10 layers

    c. A total of $100 \times 10 = 1000$ boxes could be stored in the warehouse.

27. Note: This problem would make a good class discussion. For background on effects of changing attributes—similar prisms, see page 6.

    a. The volume of a 1-2-3 box is 6 ft^3. The volume of a 1-2 cylinder is about 6.28 ft^3. The cylinder's volume is a little more than the box's volume.

    b. The surface area of a 1-2-3 box is 16 ft^2. The surface area of a 1-2 cylinder is about 15.7 ft^2. The cylinder requires a little less material than the box.

    c. Mary's class needs a cylinder with twice the volume of a 1-2 cylinder. There are infinite sets of dimensions that would work; two are a 1-4 cylinder and a 1.41-2 cylinder.

28. a. Some possible sketches:

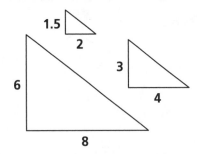

    b. If you double the length of the legs of the triangle to create a similar triangle, the larger triangle will have an area that is four times as large as the original.

29. a. 120 yd $\times$ 53$\frac{1}{3}$ yd = 6,400 yd^2

    b. 360 ft $\times$ 160 ft = 57,600 ft^2

    c. The number of square feet is 9 times the number of square yards.

    d. If the unit used to measure the length is decreased to a unit $\frac{1}{3}$ the size of the original, then the new area will be $\frac{1}{9}$ the area of the original. This happens because as you convert from yards to feet, you triple the number of needed length units (120×3) and width units ($53\frac{1}{3} \times 3$) for the new area. This new area problem is the original ($120 \times 53\frac{1}{3}$) multiplied by (3×3), or 3^2.

30. Volume = 45 cubic units; surface area = 78 square units

31. Volume = 2 cubic units; surface area = 10 square units

32. Volume = 9 cubic units; surface area = 30 square units

33. $3\frac{3}{8}$; $\frac{3}{4} \div \frac{2}{9} = 3\frac{3}{8}$

34. a. 6 cans   **b.** 36 ft^2

Extensions

35. a. Possible sketch:

b. If the parallelogram is the front of the prism, as in this example, the base would be a rectangle. In this case, you would need to measure the length and width of the rectangular base and the height of the parallelogram. The volume would be the product of these three measures.

c. You would need to find the measures of the length (l) and width (w) of the base, the length of the diagonal side (d) of the parallelogram, and the height (h) of the parallelogram. The area of the base is lw. The area of the front is wh. The area of the side is ld. The surface area is then: $2(lw + wh + ld)$.

36. Answers will vary. Students will probably discover that larger boxes tend to be better buys because the cost per unit volume is less. (Note: This ACE question makes a good project. Students will spend time collecting and analyzing real data and writing a report.)

37. a. A rectangular prism can be sliced in an infinite number of ways to produce two pieces of equal volume.

b. A cube can be sliced in an infinite number of ways to produce two pieces of equal volume.

38. a. 2 to 1   **b.** 2 to 1
c. 4 to 1   **d.** 8 to 1

39. a. 3 to 1   **b.** 3 to 1
c. 9 to 1   **d.** 27 to 1

40. a. 4 to 1   **b.** 4 to 1
c. 16 to 1   **d.** 64 to 1

Possible Answers to Mathematical Reflections

1. There are several ways to make the volume of a box eight times as large. For example, you could multiply one of the dimensions by eight. This would make the original volume ($\ell \times w \times h$) eight times as large with (8ℓ) $\times w \times h$. Another possibility is to use factors of 8 across the dimensions such as $\ell \times 4w \times 2h$ or $2\ell \times 2w \times 2h$. This last example, $2\ell \times 2w \times 2h$, where each dimension is multiplied by the same number, would create a similar box with eight times the volume.

2. If the dimensions of a rectangular prism are doubled, the new surface area is 4 times the original and the new volume is 8 times the original. If the dimensions are tripled, the new surface area is 9 times the original and the new volume is 27 times the original. If the dimensions are quadrupled, the new surface area is 16 times the original and the new volume is 64 times the original. In general, if the dimensions are multiplied by n, the new surface area is n^2 times the original and the new volume is n^3 times the original.

Answers to Looking Back and Looking Ahead

1. a. The dimensions are 16 cm by 8 cm by 32 cm.

b. The surface area is 1,792 square cm.

c. The volume is 4,096 cubic cm.

d. Answers will vary. Possible nets:

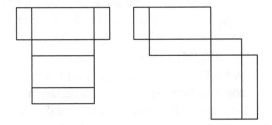

2. a. The rectangular prism with maximum surface area (and whole-number dimensions) is 1 in. by 1 in. by 40 in. The surface area is 162 sq. in.

b. The rectangular prism with the minimum surface area (and whole-number dimensions) is 2 in. by 4 in. by 5 in. The surface area is 76 sq. in.

c. Answers will vary. Possible sketches: (Figure 2).

d. If the dimensions of the box are doubled then there will be 280 more caramels. This makes 8 times as many caramels as in the original box.

3. a. 90π cubic inches or 282.74 in.^{3}

b. The volume of the rectangular prism is approximately 180 in.^{3} So the difference is $282.74 - 180$ or about 103 in.^{3}

c. The new rectangular prism should cost $1.39. The cost per cubic inch for each container is about $0.008 (from $2.19 \div 90\pi$).

d. There are many possibilities. A cone with the same volume as the cylinder could have a height of 10 inches and a radius approximately equal to 5.2 in. or a height of 9 in. and a radius approximately equal to 5.5 in. Each of these is close in height and radius to the original cylinder. Note: Due to the approximation of π or square roots, the volumes are not exactly equal.

4. The volume of a solid figure tells you the number of unit cubes that will completely fill the solid figure. The surface area is the total area of the faces of the solid figure. It tells you how much wrapping is needed to exactly cover the solid figure.

5. a. The volume of the rectangular prism can be found by the calculation: $\ell \times w \times h$. The surface area can be found by the calculation: $2(\ell \times w + \ell \times h + w \times h)$ or $2\ell \times w + 2\ell \times h + 2w \times h$.

b. The volume of the cylinder can be found by the calculation: $\pi \times r \times r \times h$ or $\pi r^2 h$. The surface area can be found by the calculation: $2\pi r^2 + 2\pi rh$.

6. The volume of the rectangular prism can be found by the calculation: $\ell \times w \times h$. The calculation $\ell \times w$ states how many unit cubes will fit on the first layer and h is the number of layers needed to fill the prism. The surface area can be found by finding the area of each of the six faces which is the calculation: $2(\ell \times w + \ell \times h + w \times h)$ or $2\ell \times w + 2\ell \times h + 2w \times h$.
The volume of the cylinder can be found by the calculation: $h \times r \times r \times \pi$ or $\pi \times r^2 \times h$. The area of the base is $\pi \times r^2$. This calculation gives the number of unit cubes that will fit on the first layer and h is the number of layers needed to fill the cylinder.
The surface area can be found by finding the area of the two circular bases and the lateral surface area. The area of the two bases is $2\pi r^2$ and the lateral surface area is the area of a rectangle whose height is h and width is the circumference of the circular base. So the surface area is $2\pi r^2 + 2\pi rh$.

Figure 2

40

7. If a cylinder, cone, and sphere have the same radius and the height of the cone and cylinder are equal, then the volume of a cone is $\frac{1}{3}$ the volume of the cylinder and $\frac{1}{2}$ the volume of the sphere. The sphere is $\frac{2}{3}$ the volume of the cylinder. Students may say it takes three cones to fill a cylinder. It takes 2 cones to fill a sphere.

8. If you know the volume of an object, it is not possible to determine its surface area. For example, if a rectangular box has a volume of 512 cubic inches, then there are many boxes with different dimensions that have a volume of 512 cubic inches. For example, a cube with side lengths of 8 inches, or a rectangular box whose dimensions are 16 in., 4 in., and 8 in. or 2 in., 32 in., and 8 in. all have a volume of 512 cubic inches. Packaging caramels in Problem 2 is another example.

   Similarly, if the surface area is known, then there are many possibilities for the volume. For example, if the surface area is 600 square cm, then a cube with side lengths of 10 cm or a rectangular box with dimensions 5 cm, 20 cm, and 8 cm have a surface area of 600 square cm.

Note: It is more difficult for students to find different boxes with the same surface area.

Some students may observe that, for certain shapes, we *can* know volume by knowing the surface area and vice versa. If we have a cube with a surface area of 150 cm^2, we know that each face is 25 cm^2, so the side length must be 5 cm, giving a volume of 125 cm^3. If we are free to make *any* rectangular prism with this surface area, we cannot know the volume, but if we are restricted to a cube we can. The same goes for spheres.

9. If two solid figures are similar and the scale factor is s, then the volume of the larger solid is s times the dimensions of the smaller solid, or $s\ell \times sw \times sh$. In other words, the volume of the larger solid is s^3 times the volume of the smaller solid. The surface area of the larger solid is s^2 times the surface area of the smaller solid. In Problem 2, part (e), the dimensions of the box are doubled, thus the number of caramels in the larger box is 40×2^3, or 320 caramels. The surface area for the box with the least surface is 76×2^2, or 304 sq. in.

Assigning the Unit Project

For this project, students are asked to design 3 different-sized packages for ping-pong balls. The project provides students with an opportunity to think further about the relationship between surface area, volume, and the shape of the container. Because the students are asked to make models of the containers, they are often surprised by just how much the surface area changes as the size of the package must change to hold more ping-pong balls. Ping-pong balls offer a nice context for the problem because some students design cylinders and others design prisms.

It is recommended that the project be done in groups of two or three. Some teachers have groups of students design and make models of the containers, work on the written proposal together, but have each student in the group turn in their own final proposal.

Commonly available mathematics class materials should be available, such as calculators, rulers, compasses, centimeter grid paper, tape, scissors, etc. In addition, students should have access to ping-pong balls so that they can test their package designs.

It is recommended that the project be launched near the end of the unit, sometime after Investigation 5. Although this project will take several hours to complete, most of the work could be done outside of class. Teachers may want to take half a class period to get students started; form groups and have them brainstorm their package designs. Then, two or three days later, after students have had some time to try out some of their ideas, teachers may want to give another half a class period for students to complete their designs. Draft work on the proposal can be done at home. Teachers can give 10 minutes at the end of the next couple of class periods for groups to get together and revise their proposals.

Some teachers have the groups share their package designs with the class, as if they were making an oral presentation to the company. To save time, some teachers pair groups together and have each group give a presentation to the other group. This gives students practice in making oral presentations yet takes considerably less time.

The blackline masters for the project and the order blank are provided. Depending on the time you have for students to work on the project, you may choose to assign only Part I. Below is a scoring rubric. This is followed by samples of student work for Part I and a teacher's comments on each sample.

Grading the Unit Project

A possible scoring rubric and two sample projects with teacher comments follow.

Suggested Scoring Rubric

The rubrics that follow are written as if Worldwide Sporting Company were evaluating the students' projects. The evaluation consists of two reviews. The first review is essentially a checklist that lets students know whether their proposal has met the company's requirements. The second review is a more thorough evaluation of their mathematics and presentation of ideas, with greater weight placed on the demonstration of mathematical ideas. The teacher who developed these rubrics had her students work in teams but write individual reports. Thus, each student's work was evaluated using these rubrics.

If this were a real review conducted by a real company, entrants who did not meet the requirements of the first review would probably be dropped from the contest. In this learning experience, however, students who do not pass the first review are asked to revise their work until it does pass. All work will eventually be evaluated using both rubrics.

The teacher who developed these rubrics gave students two grades, one for each review. The first grade was based on the score each student received for the first review. (A student's original work was used to determine this grade regardless of whether the student had to revise the work.) The second grade was based on the score each student received for the final review. (Because students could not reach this level until they had passed the first review, only work that had passed the first review was graded using this rubric.)

Sample Packages

The following sample packages will help you review the packages your students design.

Table-tennis balls are $1\frac{1}{2}$ inches, or approximately 3.8 cm, in diameter. The sample packages below and on the next page assume a diameter of 4 cm. In the table, d = diameter and h = height.

Sample Two-ball Packages

Shape	Dimensions (cm)	Surface Area (cm²)	Cost	Cost per Ball	Package
Cylinder	$d = 4$ $b = 8$	125.7	62.8¢	31.4¢	
Rectangular prism	4 by 4 by 8	160	80¢	40¢	

Sample Four-ball Packages

Shape	Dimensions (cm)	Surface Area (cm²)	Cost	Cost per Ball	Package
Cylinder	$d = 4$ $b = 16$	226.2	$1.13	28.3¢	
Rectangular prism	4 by 8 by 8	256	$1.28	32¢	
Rectangular prism	4 by 4 by 16	288	$1.44	36¢	

Sample Eight-ball Packages

Shape	Dimensions (cm)	Surface Area (cm²)	Cost	Cost per Ball	Package
Cylinder	$d = 4$ $b = 32$	427.3	$2.14	26.7¢	
Rectangular prism	8 by 8 by 8	384	$1.92	24¢	

Grading Scales

The teacher used the following grading scales for the two parts of the project.

First Review

Points	Grade
8 to 9	A
7	B
6	C
4 to 5	D

Note: Students who did not receive an A on the first review had to revise their work before it entered the final review.

Final Review

Points	Grade
24 to 27	A
20 to 23	B
16 to 19	C
12 to 15	D

First Review of Your Package Designs

Thank you, _____, for submitting a set of package designs for our table-tennis balls. Below is a summary of your project's review by our evaluators. This first review evaluates whether you met the requirements for the contest.

Does the proposal include the following?

Packages in three sizes (small, medium, and large)	❏ yes	❏ no
Description of the shapes of the packages	❏ yes	❏ no
Explanation of why these shapes were selected	❏ yes	❏ no
Cost per package	❏ yes	❏ no
Description of the cost-efficiency of the designs	❏ yes	❏ no
Description of appeal and stackability of the designs	❏ yes	❏ no

Are patterns that could produce the described containers included?

Small pattern	❏ yes	❏ no
Medium pattern	❏ yes	❏ no
Large pattern	❏ yes	❏ no

Each circled yes earns 1 point. You must have earned 8 or 9 points to move on to the next level of review. Your score is _____ points.

_____ Congratulations! Your project has made it through the first review. You are now in the finals for the scholarship judging.

_____ Our evaluators feel that your project does not meet the requirements set by our company. Please revise and resubmit your design.

Sincerely,

Worldwide Sporting Company

Final Review of the Package Designs

In the final review, entries are judged in three categories: shape selection, measurement, and presentation. Use the rubrics below to assign a score from 0 to 3 to each item in the categories at the right.

Rubric for Shape Selection and Measurement

3 COMPLETE RESPONSE (MEETS THE DEMANDS OF THE PROJECT)

- Shows understanding of the mathematical concepts and procedures
- Satisfies all essential conditions of the problem

2 PARTIAL RESPONSE (WORK NEEDS SOME REVISION)

- Shows some understanding of the mathematical concepts and procedures
- Satisfies most of the essential conditions of the problem

1 INADEQUATE RESPONSE (STUDENT NEEDS SOME INSTRUCTION TO REVISE WORK)

- Shows little understanding of the mathematical concepts and procedures
- Fails to address the essential conditions of problem

0 NO ATTEMPT

- Irrelevant response
- Does not address the conditions of the problem

Rubric for Presentation

3 COMPLETE RESPONSE (MEETS THE DEMANDS OF THE PROJECT)

- Complete, with clear, coherent work and written explanation

2 PARTIAL RESPONSE (WORK NEEDS SOME REVISION)

- Reasonably complete; may lack detail or clarity in work or written explanation

1 INADEQUATE RESPONSE (STUDENT NEEDS SOME INSTRUCTION TO REVISE WORK)

- Incomplete; work or written explanation is insufficient or not understandable

Shape Selection

CRITERIA FOR JUDGING PACKAGE SHAPES

- Stackability (0–3 points)
- Appeal (0–3 points)
- Cost-effectiveness (0–3 points)

Measurements

CRITERIA FOR JUDGING MEASUREMENTS IN STUDENTS' REPORTS

- Measurements are correct for the patterns (0–3 points)
- Measurements are reasonable (table-tennis balls will fit—packages could be slightly larger than actual table-tennis balls, but they cannot be smaller) (0–3 points)
- Amount of material (surface area) is correct for the patterns (numbers may be reasonably rounded) (0–3 points)
- Material cost per package is correct (0–3 points)

Presentation

WRITTEN PROPOSAL AND OTHER SUBMITTED WORK

- Neat, easy to read (0–3 points)
- Organized, easy to follow and to find information (0–3 points)

Sample 1

Dear World Wide Sporting Company,

I saw your contest for making ping-pong ball containers. I started working on a small, medium, and large container.
The first thing I did was to measure how tall a ping-pong ball was. I discovered it was 4 cm tall. Since it is a sphere and spheres are perfectly round, I knew it was also 4 cm wide. Then I took out 1 cm graph paper. I made a box that was 4 * 4 * 4 cm. I checked to see if a ping-pong ball would fit in it and it did.
Then I started to make the packages. I made the small package hold two balls. I made it a 4 * 8 * 4 cm box. It was in the shape of a rectangle so it would be easy to stack. There were 5 sections of 4 * 8 cm on the flat pattern. So to find the surface area I did (4 * 8) * 5. That equaled 160 sq cm for the surface area. To find the price I multiplied 160 * 0.005. That equaled $0.80 for the packaging cost.
I chose the medium package to hold 4 balls. It was a 8 * 8 * 4 cm box. It's an easily stackable rectangle. To figure out the surface area I looked and saw there were four 4 * 8 cm sides. It also had two 8 * 8 cm sides. So my equation was (4 * 8 * 4) + (8 * 8 * 2). That equaled 256 sq cm for the surface area. So to figure out the cost I took 256 * 0.005. That equaled $1.28 for packaging costs.
I had the large container fit 8 balls. It was the most cost efficient because it was a cube. It was also cheaper because I had each ball take up 3.75 cubic cm instead of 4 cubic cm. It is a 7.5 * 7.5 * 7.5 cm. The flat pattern had six 7.5 * 7.5 cm sides. So I multiplied 7.5 * 7.5 * 6. That equaled 337.5 sq cm for the surface area. Then I took 337.5 * 0.005. That equaled $1.69 and 3/4 of a cent for packaging costs.
So these are the ping pong boxes I chose. They are easily stackable and cost efficient.

Sincerely,
Jordon
Jordon

Balls Held	Dimensions	Packaging Cost	Cost Per Ball
2	4*8*4	$0.80	$0.40
4	8*8*4	$1.28	$0.32
8	7.5*7.5*7.5	$1.6875	$0.2109375

A Teacher's Comments on Jordan's Project

First Review

Jordon's report somewhat addresses each of the concerns presented by WWS, though it does not directly explain why the shape he selects for his containers is a reasonable shape (in terms of its shape) or how the shape of his container has appeal. I made small comments on these two issues to let him know what his report was lacking. I thought about having him revise his work but decided not to. This project was assigned to my students during the second semester. As a class, we have spent a lot of time talking about the quality of their work. I have given my students several opportunities to revise and have tried to push them to raise their standards. I decided to let Jordon's work go to the final review stage as is and have him deal with the comments and scores he receives in the final review.

Final Review

Jordon earned 19 of the 27 points for the final review, for a C+. Jordon was surprised by this but, after reading the comments, he seemed to understand the grading. Jordon is a bright student but sometimes settles for less-than-thorough work.

His score was reduced because he never mentions the appeal of his package design from either a customer's or a manufacturing point of view. He makes no attempt in his report to convince WWS to select his package designs. Also, his report is not well-organized. It is difficult for the reader to make sense of some of the numbers he presents. For example, he states there are 5 sections of 4-by-8 rectangles in his flat pattern for his small box. Actually, there are 3 sections that are 4 by 8, 1 section that is 4 by 7, and 1 section that is 4 by 9. The last two sections of the pattern make up one side and part of the top of the box. None of this is explained in his report. Another mathematical problem in his report is that he first uses 4 cm for the diameter of the balls and then, for the larger packages, he uses 3.75 cm. He does not explain why he has changed the number he is using for the diameter of the ball.

Sample 2

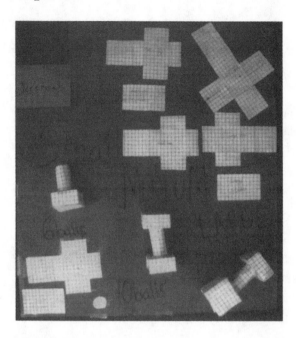

A Teacher's Comments on Jeremiah's Project

First Review

Jeremiah's report addresses each of the concerns presented by WWS except for the cost-efficiency of the design. Jeremiah also created actual models of his designs, not just patterns. Although that is not rewarded in this first review, this does affect the number of points he receives in the final review.

Final Review

Jeremiah earned 22 of the 27 points for the final review, for a B. Jeremiah lost points for the stackability of his packages but gained points for appeal, not just because of the unusual shape but because of his explanation for why his packages are appealing. The cost of each package is reasonable based on the numbers he uses (3.5 cm for the diameter of a table-tennis ball). However, the packages are really too small to hold actual table-tennis balls; Jeremiah loses points from the measurement section because of this. The added complexity of putting these packages together and the extra material needed to fasten the sections together is not mentioned, but I feel that these ideas are beyond the consideration of most seventh-graders.

UNIT PROJECT

Unit Project

The Package Design Contest

The Worldwide Sporting Company (WSC) wants a new set of package designs for their table-tennis balls (Ping-Pong balls). The table-tennis balls are about 3.8 centimeters in diameter. WSC has decided to offer a scholarship to the students or groups of students who convince the company to use their design.

- The board of directors wants a small package, a medium package, and a large package of table-tennis balls.

- The president of the company wants the cost of the packages to be considered.

- The marketing division wants the packages to be appealing to customers, to stack easily, and to look good on store shelves.

Part 1: Design a Contest Entry

You are to prepare an entry for the package design contest. Your task is to design three different packages for table-tennis balls. Include the following things in your contest entry:

1. A description of the shape or shapes of the packages you have designed and an explanation for why you selected these shapes.

2. Nets for each of your packages that, when they are cut out, folded, and taped together, will make models of your packages. Use centimeter grid paper to make your patterns.

3. Calculations of how much each of your package designs will cost to construct. The packaging material costs $0.005 per square centimeter.

Notes _____

_____

_____

_____

Part 2: Write a Report

You will submit your designs and a written proposal to WSC. Your written proposal should try to convince WSC that your designs are the ones they should use.

4. An explanation of how you have addressed WSC's three concerns (listed above).

Remember, you are trying to persuade WSC that your designs are the best and that they should select your work. Your report is to be written to the company officials. You need to think about the presentation of your written proposal. It should be neat (maybe even typed!), well organized, and easy to read so that the company officials can follow your work and ideas easily.

Unit Project The Design Contest **77**

Notes _____

_____

_____

_____

Looking Back and Looking Ahead

While working on the problems in this unit, you developed strategies for finding *surface area*, *volume*, and *nets* for rectangular prisms and cylinders. You used the relationships of other figures to cylinders to find the volumes of shapes such as *cones, spheres,* and *square pyramids.* Finally, you discovered the effects of enlargement and reduction on dimensions, surface area, and volume of prisms.

Go Online
PHSchool.com

For: Vocabulary Review Puzzle
Web Code: anj-6051

Use Your Understanding: Volume and Surface Area

To test your understanding of volume and surface area, consider the following problems.

1. Below is a net for a rectangular prism.

16 cm

16 cm

8 cm

|←———— 48 cm ————→|

    a. What are the dimensions of the box that can be made from the net?

    b. What is the surface area of the box?

    c. What is the volume of the box?

    d. Draw two other nets that will produce boxes of the same size and shape.

Notes _____

_____

_____

_____

2. Sweet-Smile Chocolates is marketing a special assortment of caramels. The company wants to put the 40 individual caramels into a rectangular box. Each caramel is a 1-inch cube. The caramels should completely fill the box.

    a. Which arrangement of caramels requires the most cardboard for a box?

    b. Which arrangement of caramels requires the least cardboard?

    c. Make sketches of the boxes you described in parts (a) and (b). Label the dimensions.

    d. Suppose each dimension of the box in part (b) is doubled. How many more caramels can be packaged in the new box?

3. The Just-Add-Water Company has decided to change the packaging for a juuice drink. The drink used to come in cylindrical containers with a base diameter of 6 inches and a height of 10 inches. The new container is a square prism that fits inside the old cylinder, as shown in the sketch.

    a. What is the volume of the original cylindrical container?

    b. How much less juice can the rectangular prism hold than the cylindrical container?

    c. Suppose that the cost per cubic inch of juice is to be the same for both containers. The original container of juice cost $2.19. How much should a new box of juice cost if the amount of juice per dollar is the same?

    d. The company is also considering selling the juice in a cone with the same volume as the cylinder. Describe the possible dimensions for such a cone.

10 in.

6 in.

4.24 in.

Notes _____

_____

_____

_____

Explain Your Reasoning

To answer problems about surface area and volume of solid figures, you
have to know the meaning of those terms and some strategies for
calculating the measurements from given dimensions of various figures.

4. What do *volume* and *surface area* measurements tell about a
solid figure?

5. Which formulas will show how to find the surface area A and the
volume V of each figure?

    a. a rectangular prism   **b.** a cylinder

6. How can you convince someone that the formulas given in
Exercise 5 are correct?

7. How are the volumes of cylinders, cones, and spheres related?

8. a. Suppose you know the volume of an object such as a box, a
cylinder, or a cone. Can you determine its surface area?

    b. Suppose you know the surface area of an object. Can you
find the volume?

9. How are the surface areas and volumes of square pyramids
related to cubes?

Look Ahead

Measurement of surface area and volume for solid figures is used in many
practical, scientific, and engineering problems. You will encounter the key
ideas about area and volume in future *Connected Mathematics* units, in
other mathematics subjects such as geometry, and in many situations of
daily life such as packing, storing, and building tasks.

Notes _____

_____

_____

_____

B

base The face of a three-dimensional shape chosen to be the "bottom" face.

base La cara de una figura tridimensional elegida para que sea la cara de la "base."

C

cone A three-dimensional shape with a circular base and a vertex opposite the base.

cono Figura tridimensional con una base circular y un vértice opuesto a la base.

cube A three-dimensional shape with six identical square faces.

cubo Una figura tridimensional con seis caras cuadradas idénticas.

cylinder A three-dimensional shape with two opposite faces that are congruent circles. The side (lateral surface) is a rectangle that is "wrapped around" the circular faces at the ends.

cilindro Una figura tridimensional con dos caras opuestas que son círculos congruentes. El lado (la cara lateral) rectángulo es un está "envuelto alrededor de" que las dos caras circulares es los extremos.

Notes _____

E

edge A line segment formed where two faces of a three-dimensional shape meet.

arista El segmento de recta formado donde se encuentran dos caras de una figura tridimensional.

edge

edge

F

face A flat two-dimensional surface of a three-dimensional shape.

cara Superficie plana, bidimensional de una figura tridimensional.

H

height The vertical distance between the face chosen to be the base and

- the opposite face of a prism or cylinder, or
- the vertex of a cone or pyramid.

altura La distencia vertical entre la cara elegida para ser base y

- la cara opuesta de un prisma o cilindro, o
- el vértice de un cono o pirámide.

height

height

height

height

N

net A two-dimensional pattern that can be folded into a three-dimensional figure.

patrón plano Un patrón bidimensional que se puede plegar para formar una figura tridimensional.

82 Filling and Wrapping

Notes _____

_____

_____

_____

oblique prism A prism whose side faces are non-rectangular parallelograms.

prisma oblicuo Prisma cuyas caras laterales son paralelogramos no rectangulares.

prism A three-dimensional shape with a top and bottom (base) that are congruent polygons and lateral faces that are parallelograms.

prisma Una figura tridimensional cuya parte superior y cuyo fondo (base) son polígonos congruentes y cuyas caras laterales son paralelogramos.

pyramid A three-dimensional shape with one polygonal base and lateral sides that are all triangles that meet at a vertex opposite the base.

pirámide Figura tridimensional cuya base es un polígono y cuyas caras laterales son tríangulos que se encuentran en un vértice opuesto a la base.

rectangular prism A prism with a top and bottom (base) that are congruent rectangles.

prisma rectangular Un prisma cuya parte superior e inferior (base) son rectángulos congruentes.

Right rectangular prism

Oblique rectangular prism

English/Spanish Glossary **83**

Notes _____

_____

_____

_____

right prism A prism whose vertical faces are rectangles. The bases are congruent polygons.

prisma recto Un prisma cuyas caras verticales son rectángulos. Los bases son polígonos congruentes.

sphere A three-dimensional shape whose surface consists of all the points that are a given distance from the center of the shape.

esfera Una figura tridimensional cuya superficie consiste en todos los puntos ubicados a una distancia dada del centro de la figura.

surface area The area required to cover a three-dimensional shape.

área total El área requerida para cubrir una figura tridimensional.

unit cube A cube whose edges are 1 unit long. It is the basic unit of measurement for volume.

unidad cúbica Un cubo cuyas aristas miden 1 unidad de longitud. Es la unidad básica de medición para el volumen.

volume The amount of space occupied by, or the capacity of, a three-dimensional shape. The volume is the number of unit cubes that will fit into a three-dimensional shape.

volumen La cantidad de espacio que ocupa una figura tridimensional o la capacidad de dicha figura. Es el número de unidades cúbicas que cabrán en una figura tridimensional.

STUDENT PAGE

Notes _____

_____

_____

_____

Academic Vocabulary

Academic vocabulary words are words that you see in textbooks and on tests. These are not math vocabulary terms, but knowing them will help you succeed in mathematics.

Las palabras de vocabulario académico son palabras que ves en los libros de texto y en las pruebas. Éstos no son términos de vocabulario de matemáticas, pero conocerlos te ayudará a tener éxito en matemáticas.

C

compare To tell or show how two things are alike and different.

related terms: analyze, relate, resemble

Sample: Compare the volumes of the cube and the rectangular prism.

The volume of the cube is 3 ft × 3 ft × 3 ft = 27 ft³. The volume of the rectangular prism is 2 ft × 2 ft × 7 ft = 28 ft³. The rectangular prism has 1 cubic foot more volume than the cube.

comparar Decir o mostrar en qué se parecen o en qué se diferencian dos cosas.

términos relacionados: analizar, relacionar, asemejar

Ejemplo: Compara el volumen del cubo con el del prisma rectangular.

El volumen del cubo es 3 pies × 3 pies × 3 pies = 27 pies³. El volumen del prisma rectangular es 2 pies × 2 pies × 7 pies = 28 pies³. El prisma rectangular tiene 1 pie cúbico más de volumen que el cubo.

D

describe To explain or tell in detail. A written description can contain facts and other information needed to communicate your answer. A diagram or a graph may also be included.

related terms: express, explain

Sample: Describe how to determine the surface area of a square pyramid.

Find the area of the square base by squaring the side length. Next, find the area of one of the triangle faces using the formula $A = \frac{1}{2}bh$, where b is the length of the base and h is the height of the triangle. Next, multiply the area of the triangle by 4, since there are four congruent triangle faces. The sum of the areas of the faces and the base is the surface area of the square pyramid.

describir Explicar o decir con detalles. Una descripción escrita puede tener datos e información necesaria para comunicar tu respuesta. Puedes incluir un diagrama o una gráfica.

términos relacionados: expresar, explicar

Ejemplo: Describe cómo se determina el área superficial de una pirámide cuadrada.

Halla el área de la base cuadrada, elevando al cuadrado la longitud de lado. Luego, halla el área de una de las caras triangulares usando la fórmula $A = \frac{1}{2}bh$, donde b es la longitud de la base y h es la altura del triángulo. Después, multiplica el área del triángulo por 4, ya que hay cuatro caras triangulares congruentes. La suma de las áreas de las caras y de la base es el área superficial de la pirámide cuadrada.

Academic Vocabulary **85**

Notes _____

_____

_____

_____

estimate To find an approximate answer that is relatively close to an exact amount.

related terms: approximate, guess

Sample: Estimate the volume of the smoothie cup.

4 in.

6 in.

3 in.

The smoothie cup is approximately the shape of a cylinder with a height of 6 inches. I can find the average of the top and bottom base diameters, which is (4 + 3) ÷ 2 or 3.5 inches. So, I will use the radius of 1.75 inches to estimate the volume. The volume of the smoothie cup is about $6 \times 1.75^2 \times \pi$, or about 57.7 cm³.

estimar Hallar una respuesta aproximada, relativamente cercana a una cantidad exacta.

términos relacionados: aproximar, adivinar

Ejemplo: Estima el volumen del vaso de licuado.

4 pulg.

6 pulg.

3 pulg.

El vaso de licuado tiene la forma aproximada de un cilindro con altura de 6 pulgadas. Puedo hallar el promedio de los diámetros de la boca y de la base, el cual es (4 + 3) ÷ 2 ó 3.5 pulgadas. Por lo tanto, usaré el radio de 1.75 pulgadas para estimar el volumen. El volumen del vaso de licuado es aproximadamente $6 \times 1.75^2 \times \pi$, o aproximadamente 57.7 cm³.

---

explain To give facts and details that make an idea easier to understand. Explaining can involve a written summary supported by a diagram, chart, table, or a combination of these.

related terms: describe, analyze, clarify, describe, justify, tell

Sample: Explain what shape can be formed if the net below is assembled.

The net has two congruent circles and a rectangle, so this is a cylinder when it is assembled. The two circles form bases, and the rectangle can be rolled to form the cylinder.

explicar Dar datos y detalles que facilitan el entendimiento de una idea. Explicar puede requerir la preparación de un informe escrito apoyado por un diagrama, una tabla, un esquema o una combinación de éstos.

términos relacionados: describir, analizar, aclarar, justificar, decir

Ejemplo: Explica qué figura se puede formar si se arma el patrón que se ve abajo.

El patrón tiene dos círculos congruentes y un rectángulo, por lo tanto, cuando se arma es un cilindro. Los dos círculos forman bases y el rectángulo se puede enrollar para formar el cilindro.

Notes _____

_____

_____

_____

Index

Notes _____

_____

_____

_____

Notes

Acknowledgments

Team Credits

The people who made up the **Connected Mathematics 2** team—representing editorial, editorial services, design services, and production services—are listed below. Bold type denotes core team members.

Leora Adler, Judith Buice, Kerry Cashman, Patrick Culleton, Sheila DeFazio, Richard Heater, **Barbara Hollingdale, Jayne Holman,** Karen Holtzman, **Etta Jacobs,** Christine Lee, Carolyn Lock, Catherine Maglio, **Dotti Marshall,** Rich McMahon, Eve Melnechuk, Kristin Mingrone, Terri Mitchell, **Marsha Novak,** Irene Rubin, Donna Russo, Robin Samper, Siri Schwartzman, **Nancy Smith,** Emily Soltanoff, **Mark Tricca,** Paula Vergith, Roberta Warshaw, Helen Young

Additional Credits

Diana Bonfilio, Mairead Reddin, Michael Torocsik, nSight, Inc.

Technical Illustration

WestWords, Inc.

Cover Design

tom white.images

Photos

2, Getty Images, Inc.; **3,** Geri Engberg; **5,** Jeff Greenberg/PhotoEdit; **9,** Jack Kurt/The Image Works; **15,** photolibrary.com pty. ltd./Index Stock Imagery, Inc.; **16,** Digital Vision/Getty Images, Inc.; **20,** Laura Dwight/PhotoEdit; **27,** BananaStock/Robertstock; **28,** IFA/PictureQuest; **29,** Andrew Olney/Masterfile; **30,** Bob Daemmrich/PhotoEdit; **37,** Lynn Stone/Getty Images, Inc.; **39,** Danita Delimont/Alamy; **40,** Richard Haynes; **42,** Getty Images, Inc.; **45,** Sam Yeh/AFP/Getty Images, Inc.; **52,** Francis Dean/The Image Works; **53,** ©2002 Thaves. Reprinted with permission. Newspaper dist. by NEA, Inc.; **59 l,** Bryan & Cherry Alexander/Photo Researchers, Inc.; **59 r,** A. Woolfitt/Robert Harding World Imagery; **60,** Richard Haynes; **62,** David Young-Wolff/PhotoEdit; **62 inset,** Wally Eberhart/Getty Images, Inc.; **65,** Clayton Sharrard/PhotoEdit; **66,** SuperStock, Inc./SuperStock; **68,** Jeff Mermelstein/Getty Images, Inc.; **69,** Masterfile (Royalty-Free Division); **73,** Richard Haynes; **77,** Brooke Slezak/Getty Images, Inc.

Note: Every effort has been made to locate the copyright owner of the material reprinted in this book. Omissions brought to our attention will be corrected in subsequent editions.

STUDENT PAGE

Notes _____

Labsheet 1.3

Box Nets

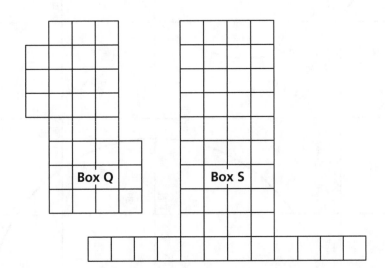

Labsheet 3.2

Filling Cylinders

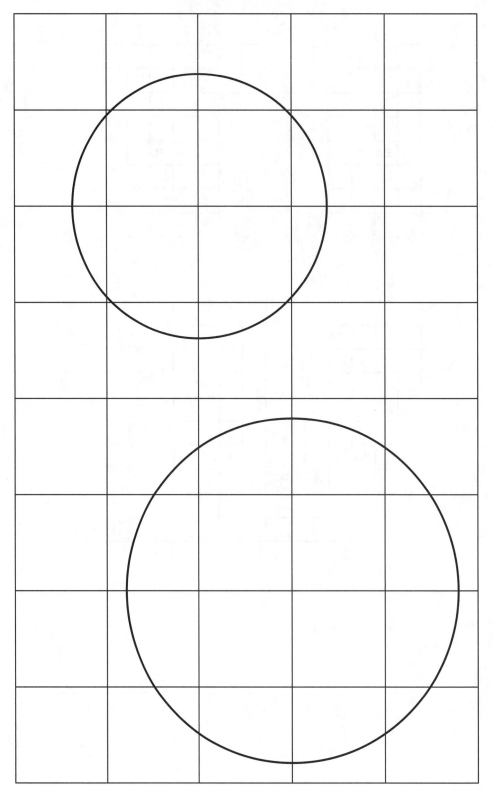

Labsheet 3.3A

Prism Nets

Filling and Wrapping

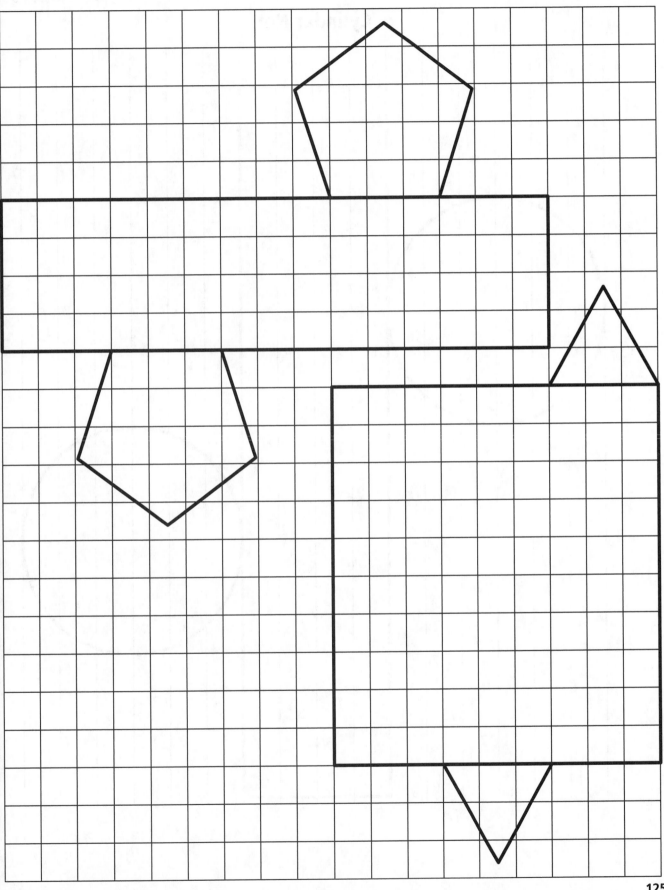

Labsheet 3.3B

Cylinder Net

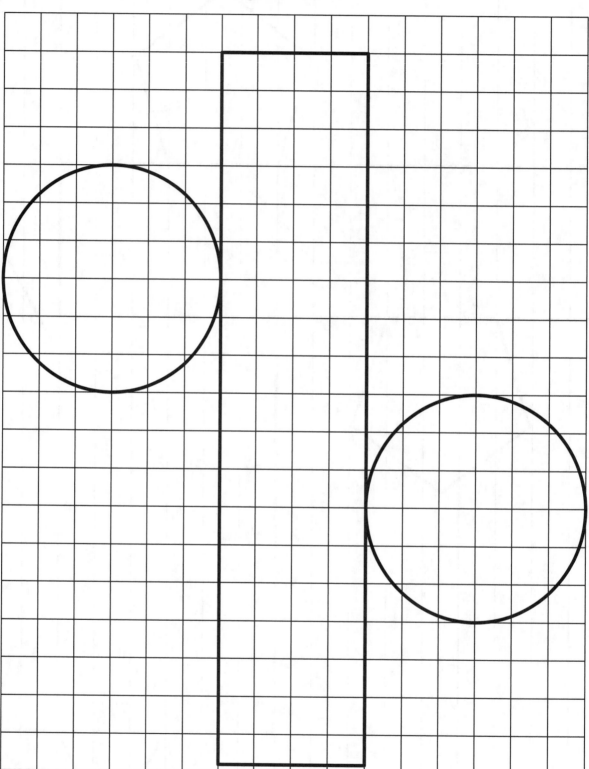

Labsheet 4.1

Centimeter Grid

Labsheet 4.2A

Net for a Cylinder

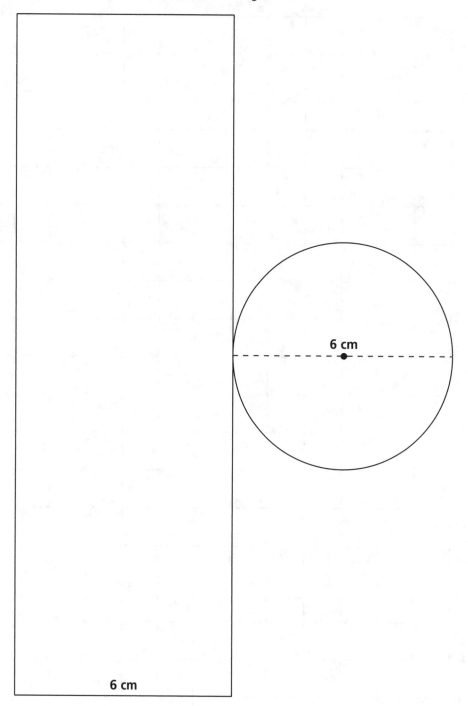

Labsheet 4.2B

Net for a Cylinder

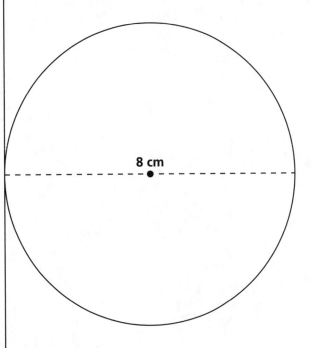

8 cm

8 cm

Labsheet 4.2C

Nets for Two Cones

Labsheet 4.2D

Net for a Prism

6 cm

6 cm

Labsheet 4.2E

· ·

Net for a Pyramid

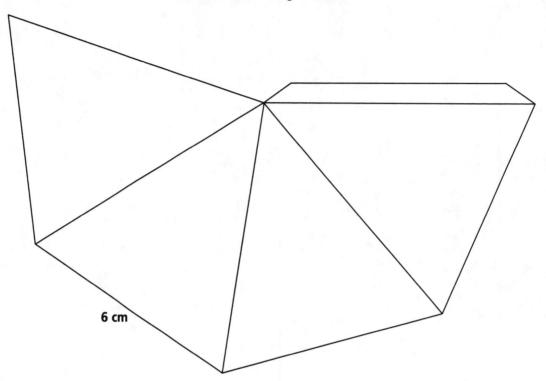

6 cm

Labsheet 5.2

....

Similar Compost Boxes

Open Box (*h-w-l*)	Scale Factor	Surface Area (sq. ft)	Volume (cu. ft)	Amount of Garbage Decomposed in One Day	Number of Worms Needed
1-2-3					
2-4-6					
3-6-9					
4-8-12					
. . .					
		1,024			
. . .					
			6,000		

PACING: _____

Mathematical Goals

_____

_____

_____

_____

Launch

Materials

_____

_____

_____

_____

_____

_____

_____

Explore

Materials

_____

_____

_____

_____

_____

_____

_____

Summarize

Materials

_____

_____

_____

_____

_____

_____

_____

Glossary

B

base The face of a three-dimensional shape chosen to be the "bottom" face.

C

cone A three-dimensional shape with a circular base and a vertex opposite the base.

cube A three-dimensional shape with six identical square faces.

cylinder A three-dimensional shape with two opposite faces that are congruent circles. The side (lateral surface) is a rectangle that is "wrapped around" the circular faces at the ends.

E

edge A line segment formed where two faces of a three-dimensional shape meet.

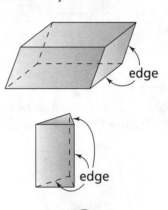

F

face A flat two-dimensional surface of a three-dimensional shape.

H

height The vertical distance between the face chosen to be the base and

- the opposite face of a prism or cylinder, or
- the vertex of a cone or pyramid.

net A two-dimensional pattern that can be folded into a three-dimensional figure.

oblique prism A prism whose side faces are non-rectangular parallelograms.

prism A three-dimensional shape with a top and bottom (base) that are congruent polygons and lateral faces that are parallelograms.

pyramid A three-dimensional shape with one polygonal base and lateral sides are all triangles that meet at a vertex opposite the base.

Triangular   Square   Pentagonal
Pyramid   Pyramid   Pyramid

rectangular prism A prism with a top and bottom (base) that are congruent rectangles.

Right   **Oblique**
rectangular   **rectangular**

right prism A prism whose vertical faces are rectangles. The bases are congruent polygons.

sphere A three-dimensional shape whose surface consists of all the points that are a given distance from the center of the shape.

surface area The area required to cover a three-dimensional shape.

unit cube A cube whose edges are 1 unit long. It is the basic unit of measurement for volume.

volume The amount of space occupied by, or the capacity of, a three-dimensional shape. The volume is the number of unit cubes that will fit into a three-dimensional shape.

Index

INDEX

Acknowledgments

Team Credits

The people who made up the **Connected Mathematics 2** team—representing editorial, editorial services, design services, and production services—are listed below. Bold type denotes core team members.

Leora Adler, Judith Buice, Kerry Cashman, Patrick Culleton, Sheila DeFazio, Richard Heater, **Barbara Hollingdale, Jayne Holman,** Karen Holtzman, **Etta Jacobs,** Christine Lee, Carolyn Lock, Catherine Maglio, **Dotti Marshall,** Rich McMahon, Eve Melnechuk, Kristin Mingrone, Terri Mitchell, **Marsha Novak,** Irene Rubin, Donna Russo, Robin Samper, Siri Schwartzman, **Nancy Smith,** Emily Soltanoff, **Mark Tricca,** Paula Vergith, Roberta Warshaw, Helen Young

Additional Credits

Diana Bonfilio, Mairead Reddin, Michael Torocsik, nSight, Inc.

Technical Illustration

Schawk, Inc.

Cover Design

tom white.images